JMG

Junior Master Gardener®

Junior Master Gardener®

Golden Ray Series_{SM} – Level 1

Health and Nutrition from the Garden_{SM}

18 USC 707

A 4-H Youth Development Program

www.jmgkids.us

For Program Information:
International JMG Program Headquarters
225 Horticulture/Forestry Building
Texas A&M University
2134 TAMU
College Station, Texas   77843-2134
(979) 845-8565
(979) 845-8906 fax
http://www.jmgkids.us

Published and Distributed by:
Texas AgriLife Extension Service
P.O. Box 1209
Bryan, Texas   77806
(888) 900-2577 toll-free
(979) 458-0172 fax
https://AgriLifebookstore.org

To order:
Go to *https://AgriLifebookstore.org*
or call (888) 900-2577 toll-free

ISBN   0-9672990-7-1   (Health and Nutrition)

CONTENTS

Gardening for Health and Nutrition

Gardening is one of America's favorite pastimes. Grandparents, mothers, fathers and youths can partake in this creative, constructive activity to produce more than just beautiful flowers. Gardening gives people of all ages a place to play, experiment and enjoy the "fruits" of their labors.

Growing fruits and vegetables in a home or community garden also provides an environment where health, nutrition, food safety and wise decision-making skills can be taught. The JMG Golden Ray Curriculum *"Health and Nutrition from the Garden"* can be used to teach and reinforce these lessons and skills.

Children can be creative and experience their world through environmental, hands-on education. Group gardening also offers youths opportunities to cross barriers of ethnicity, age and gender, and offers many positive experiences. Through these experiences, children could be inclined to sample new foods and adopt the practice of eating new and different fruits and vegetables from the garden.

This is important because most children do not eat the minimum recommended number of servings (five) of fruits and vegetables each day. Currently, most children consume only two to three servings daily of fruits and vegetables, foods that contain vitamins and minerals essential to their health and growth. Fortunately, there are many programs, such as the Five-A-Day for Better Health Program, available to encourage youths to increase their intake of fruits and vegetables.

The formative childhood years are the best time to begin healthful eating habits. If children learn at a young age to eat at least five servings of fruits and vegetables each day, then they may continue these healthful habits into their teenage and adult years.

Children also influence their parents. If parents are educated by their youngsters about gardening and growing healthful, nutritious fruits and vegetables, they and their families are more likely to spend more quality time with their children, and improve the daily intake of healthful, nutritious foods.

Gardening is also a way for families to stretch their food dollars. With a bit of seed, some soil and water, plus a little tender loving care, food gardens can keep producing over time. The garden soil is a storage area to keep many root crops nutritious and safe until needed as a meal or snack. Saving fruit and vegetable seeds for future use, using homemade paper pots, and recycling milk jugs are other ways gardeners can conserve their dollars.

Through garden projects, children learn to take great pride in their efforts, give back to their community and act as mentors to younger gardeners. Older youths are encouraged to teach and lead younger participants to garden.

Gardening is also children to get outdoors, exert energy, and use their imaginations constructively. These actions, in themselves, are reasons to garden. Many lessons in this book allow children to bend, squat, kneel, twist, walk, talk, laugh and interact with one another in their plant world. The lessons that are associated with some level of physical activity are marked with the "Body Builder" symbol.

So come on! Join in the JMG experience and help children learn about the many benefits and possibilities available through gardening. Soil your hands, get involved and teach children to garden for better health and nutrition.

PROGRAM PARTNERS

The Golden Ray Series, *Health and Nutrition from the Garden*, is made possible through the collaborative efforts of the following partners:

- Junior Master Gardener Program, Texas AgriLife Extension Service, The Texas A&M University System
- Extension Nutrition and Food Science, AgriLife Extension, The Texas A&M University System
- Vegetable and Fruit Improvement Center (VFIC), Texas A&M University

WHAT IS THE JUNIOR MASTER GARDENER® PROGRAM?

The Junior Master Gardener (JMG) program is an innovative youth gardening project/curriculum developed by the Texas AgriLife Extension Service and associated with other Cooperative Extension Services, 4-H, schools and other youth organizations across the nation. This dynamic program educates youths about horticulture, health, nutrition, environmental science, and leadership and life skills using fun, creative activities. Flexibility is a key component of the JMG program that enables it to be adapted to meet the needs and interests of different individuals and organizations.

The primary research and evaluation provider for this curriculum project is the *Growing Minds* program. This research program, developed by Dr. Jayne Zajicek, Department of Horticultural Sciences at Texas A&M University, focuses on evaluating and assessing the effects and interaction of plants and gardening on people. Nutritional attitudes on behavior, academic achievement, or life skills and leadership development in youths, and life quality of the elderly are researched. For more information: *www.jmgkids.us*

WHAT IS EXTENSION NUTRITION AND FOOD SCIENCE?

The Extension Nutrition and Food Science unit is a part of the Family and Consumer Sciences program of the Texas AgriLife Extension Service. Extension education in Family and Consumer Sciences (FCS) helps families build skills in money management; parenting; food purchase, preparation, and safety; communication and problem solving; consumer decision making; child and elder care; guiding adolescents; improving health and safety; and entrepreneurship. Extension FCS programs are designed to help individuals and families achieve economic stability, improve health and well-being, and enhance life quality through making positive changes. Family and Consumer Sciences' mission is changing families for the better.

The purpose of Extension Nutrition and Food Science is to empower Texans to improve their quality of life and fulfill their potential through the adoption of sound food and nutrition practices. Utilizing the latest in food and nutrition research and responding to current trends that affect food and nutrition, the Extension Nutrition and Food Science programs focus on the following areas: personal and family health; food safety and quality; health considerations linked to agricultural food production, processing, and distribution; food security and hunger; at risk families; consumer and public policy concerns; and 4-H youth food and nutrition.

For more information: *http://fcs.tamu.edu*

WHAT IS THE VEGETABLE AND FRUIT IMPROVEMENT CENTER?

The Vegetable and Fruit Improvement Center (VFIC) is a part of the Texas A&M University Department of Horticultural Sciences. It was established to support and strengthen the produce industry through research. Research offers great opportunities to develop new vegetables and fruits with improved nutritional and health benefits.

It is the mission of the VFIC to develop new varieties of fruits and vegetables that have health and nutrition benefits and to provide credible technical information to consumers and producers through AgriLife Extension and other agencies. For more information: *http://vic.tamu.edu*

WHAT IS A JMG® GOLDEN RAY SERIES℠?

The JMG Golden Ray Series is a part of the Junior Master Gardener program. It offers a way to expand the JMG curricula to gain in-depth training and serves as a stand-alone unit of study to provide a taste of the JMG experience. As with all JMG program curricula, the Golden Ray Series is designed to be a flexible, tri-level program:

- Level 1, Grades 3 to 5
- Level 2, Grades 6 to 8
- Level 3, Grades 9 to 12

The Golden Ray Series can be used in a variety of settings:

- public, private and home schools;
- 4-H clubs and Master Gardener projects;
- community organizations (after-school programs, summer camp, scouts);
- botanical gardens and arboreta.

Participants can be recognized for completing a Golden Ray Series of the JMG program in one of two ways. Participants can complete a stand-alone Golden Ray Series, such as *Health and Nutrition from the Garden,* or meet the expanded requirements for one of the eight chapters in the JMG Level 1 Handbook and JMG Level 1 Teacher/Leader Guide. For example, participants in a JMG group can receive a certificate for completing this stand-alone Golden Ray Series. If group participants meet all the requirements for completing a Golden Ray Series by using the JMG Level 1 Handbook and completing the chapter on landscape horticulture, the participants are eligible for a Golden Ray Series certificate for landscape horticulture. Expanded requirements for Golden Ray Series certification are detailed on the JMG Web site (*www.jmgkids.us*).

Each Golden Ray Series curriculum is divided into applicable teaching concepts. All Golden Ray Series curricula contain helpful appendices, including the registration packet, garden planning and preparation instructions, modules, worksheets and parental take-home sheets. For use by school teachers, the activities have been correlated to academic standards. Correlation of Golden Ray Series curricula and subject matter to academic standards is available on the JMG Web site at *www.jmgkids.us* or from JMG headquarters at (979) 845-8565.

WHO ADMINISTERS THE JMG® GOLDEN RAY SERIES℠ PROGRAM?

The JMG Golden Ray Series program is administered as part of the Junior Master Gardener program by the Texas AgriLife Extension Service, The Texas A&M University System, in College Station, Texas.

Locally, administration of all JMG groups is flexible. They may be administered by county Extension offices or by other local educational organizations with support from Extension. For example, a school district can organize a JMG group in its after-school child care program and access horticultural and youth development expertise and support from the local Extension office, if needed.

WHO CAN PARTICIPATE IN A JMG® GOLDEN RAY SERIES℠ PROGRAM?

Any organization with a mission of youth development and education can register a Junior Master Gardener Golden Ray Series group, including:

- schools (e.g., classroom, after-school child care and home schools)
- food stamp nutrition programs
- Vegetable and Fruit Improvement Center audiences
- community/neighborhood youth programs (e.g., Master Gardener projects, scouting/church groups, 4-H, Boys and Girls Clubs, camps, arboreta/botanical gardens, garden clubs)

Upon starting each new Golden Ray Series group, the leader should provide the state JMG headquarters with a completed registration packet.

WHAT DEFINES A GROUP?

1. A minimum of five youths
2. One or more adult teacher/leader(s)
3. Suitable meeting facilities (classroom, garden area)
4. An official club or group name (JMG office reserves the right to modify name)

To register a Junior Master Gardener group and work toward Golden Ray Series℠ certification, complete and mail the registration packet (page 173) or contact:

- a county Extension office
- JMG headquarters at (979) 845-8565
- JMG Web site at *www.jmgkids.us*

The registration packet includes the four pages needed to organize a youth group:

- Junior Master Gardener Registration Agreement Form;
- Junior Master Gardener Member Group Enrollment Form;
- Junior Master Gardener Leader/Teacher Registration Form.

These forms also can be downloaded from the JMG Web page.

Once you have a registration packet, complete each form carefully. The JMG registration packet should be mailed to the Junior Master Gardener program office. When you register, your group will be posted on the JMG Web page. As a registered group you will receive updates about local community sponsors, program partners, and national JMG program updates.

Junior Master Gardener Program
2134 TAMU
College Station, Texas 77843-2134
Phone (979) 845-8656
Fax (979) 845-8906
E-mail: *programinfo@jmgkids.us*

The JMG program office will send an official letter of registration for your group. A copy of your registration packet will be sent to your nearest Extension office for its records. Your group of young gardeners will then be ready to begin the Golden Ray Series experience of the JMG program.

After members of your group complete the JMG Golden Ray Series curriculum requirements, you can order Golden Ray Series certificates by completing the Junior Master Gardener Completion Form, and mailing it to the JMG program office at Texas A&M University. Certificates will be promptly returned for presentation to your Junior Master Gardeners!

Health and Nutrition from the Garden, as well as other JMG curricula, JMG recognition items and JMG apparel, can be ordered online at *www.jmgkids.us* or by calling (888) 900-2577.

Your Role as a Teacher/Leader

- Participate in training as needed
- Submit the JMG registration packet to the JMG program office
- Request books and remit payment
- Serve as instructor or coordinator
- Distribute information to JMG participants and parents
- Participate in evaluation and reporting of JMG activities
- Provide recognition for JMG participants

Golden Ray Series Program Policies and Guidelines

The Golden Ray Series program is a certification through the JMG program and is designed to be flexible. A successful JMG group can be managed in many ways. There are a few policies that have been established and must be adhered to by all JMG groups. These policies have been established to ensure that the objectives of the JMG program are met, and to protect the credibility of the JMG program as a youth development and education program of the Texas AgriLife Extension Service.

Service marks, copyright and logos: The terms Junior Master Gardeners, JMG, Golden Ray Series, Junior Master Series and associated logos are registered trademarks or service marks of the Texas AgriLife Extension Service, The Texas A&M University System, College Station, Texas.

The JMG Golden Ray Series *Health and Nutrition from the Garden* is copyrighted and may not be copied or duplicated without written permission from the JMG headquarters. However, any document in the appendices of the JMG Golden Ray Series *Health* and *Nutrition from the Garden* may be duplicated.

Commercialism: The Junior Master Gardener program is intended to be a noncommercial youth educational program. No individual associated with a JMG group or FVIC project may enter into a contract or relationship of a commercial nature involving the JMG program unless authorized by the JMG headquarters and state office of the Texas AgriLife Extension Service.

No local JMG group may enter into a contract or business relationship with a business, corporation or individual that may be construed as using the JMG or FVIC programs and/or their registered trademarks or service marks, logos, names or emblems to conduct, sell or give endorsement for commercial purposes. This policy is not intended to interfere with any JMG group conducting fund-raising activities to support its local projects.

Certificates and badges: JMG Golden Ray Series certificates and/or badges are to be used only by the groups and participants of the JMG program. No alterations, modifications or additions to the JMG certificates and badges can be made without written permission of the JMG headquarters of the Texas AgriLife Extension Service.

Equal opportunity statement: The Junior Master Gardener program of the Texas AgriLife Extension Service, is open to all people without regard to socioeconomic level, race, color, sex, disability, religion, age, or national origin.

Financial issues: Regarding financial matters (i.e., fund-raising, accounting, banking), JMG groups are encouraged to follow the guidelines set forth by the sponsoring organization.

Insurance: All youth groups are encouraged to secure insurance against liability and accident. Follow the procedures of the sponsoring organization for insurance guidelines and policies.

Each series curriculum contains group activities designed to enhance individual knowledge and leadership.

How do Youth become certified?

- Youth must complete 12 activities.
- It is suggested that 2 activities be selected from each teaching concept in this curriculum.
- Youth must complete 1 Lifeskill/Career Exploration activity.
- Youth must complete 1 Service Learning/Leadership project.

Upon completion of the Golden Ray Series *Health and Nutrition from the Garden*, youths will have finished 12 activities from the six teaching concepts, one life skill and career exploration activity, and one community service project.

Included in each concept of this curriculum is helpful background information, which includes general information to assist the teacher/leader in presenting the activities. Also included is a listing of other activities that can be adapted and used with your group to address the teaching concepts.

Standardized test formatted reading passages for grades three to five are also included in the appendices. Correlations to academic standards can be downloaded from the JMG Web site.

The questionnaire used in the evaluation of this curriculum was adopted from Domel, Baranowski, et.al, Preventative Medicine, 1993, 22:866-879. This evaluation tool is available at *www.jmgkids.us.*

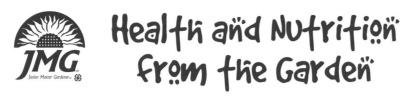

Health and Nutrition from the Garden

TEACHING CONCEPTS

Teaching Concept 1: Basic Gardening
Participants learn how to garden for optimum plant growth, production and food quality.

> P.L.A.N.T. Needs
> Small and Large
> Rules 'n' Tools
> Touchy-feely
> Pies and Shake, Rattle and Roll
> Who Goes There?

Teaching Concept 2: Growing Techniques
Participants learn about different methods used by experienced gardeners and professionals to make our world a better place.

> Paper Pots
> Paper Towel Gardening
> Make Your Pick
> Protection by Diversity
> Cylinder Gardening
> Sack of Potatoes
> Bean Tepee

Teaching Concept 3: Thrifty Gardens
Participants learn how to use their garden wisely and how to make wise choices in purchasing garden items.

> Shop 'n' Grow
> Food Storage Gardens
> Plan 10 in 2
> Seed Bank
> Swap Shop Eats

Teaching Concept 4: Food Safety
Participants learn about and use food safety practices when preparing harvested fruits and vegetables, which help to keep their foods safe and nutritious.

> Safety First
> Garden to the Table
> Bold Molds
> Party Confetti Salad
> Save It

Teaching Concept 5: ABC's of Healthful Eating
Participants learn about different fruits and vegetables that provide some essential vitamins and minerals the body needs to stay strong and healthy.

> The Pyramid
> Label Reader
> Taste Test
> Rough and Tough Foods
> U-B the Judge
> Fruit and Veggie Mania
> Beauty Contest
> Healing Powers

Teaching Concept 6: Healthful Snacks
Participants learn about and experience healthful snack alternatives to help keep them energized and active.

> Fruit and Veggie Lab
> Apple Surprise
> Symmetry Snacks II
> Robust Rainbow Recipes
> Strip Chips
> Junk Food Blues
> More Snack-time Fun

LIFE SKILLS AND CAREER EXPLORATION

Participants learn about different life skills and career opportunities.

SERVICE LEARNING AND LEADERSHIP PROJECTS

Participants learn, develop and share their new knowledge with their families, friends and community through service and leadership, which helps them develop self-sufficiency and self-sustaining skills.

GETTING STARTED

It is recommended that groups with no previous gardening experience complete several activities in the teaching concept 1–Basic Gardening. Most of these activities require the use of a garden area. Information in Basic Gardening and Growing Techniques will help you choose a garden type and location. In addition, Appendix A gives helpful information related to garden preparation and planting.

Also, each youth is encouraged to have his or her own gardening journal, included in Appendix B. The journal pages have places for young gardeners to write, draw and solve problems using their experiences in the garden. Activity worksheets from various teaching concepts can be added to their journals. This is a good way for each child to see progress and to have a record of their many adventures in the JMG Golden Ray Series.

ADDITIONAL JMG® OPPORTUNITIES

There are additional opportunities in the Junior Master Gardener Program. Youths can receive recognition in JMG by earning a Golden Ray Series certificate or earning JMG certification. Your gardeners can continue expanding their expertise and involvement within the JMG program by using the JMG Handbook and Teacher/Leader Guide. The JMG Level 1 curriculum covers many aspects of horticulture, including plant growth and development, soils and water, ecology and environmental horticulture, insects and diseases, landscape horticulture, fruits and nuts, vegetables and herbs, life skills and career exploration. More information about JMG certification and additional topics is available on the JMG Web site at *www.jmgkids.us* or by contacting the International JMG Program Headquarters at (979) 845-8565.

*JMG...Cultivating youth and communities through gardening*sm

CHILDREN'S GARDENING

The JMG Program allows youths to work together as a team, sharing the responsibilities of building a vegetable garden, learning the nutritional content of fruits and vegetables, and calculating basic gardening economics. For a team working toward common goals, a group gardening project can provide a sense of community, belonging and acceptance. In addition, during the course of this study, students will have the opportunity to develop and practice leadership skills and serve their community.

TIPS AND SUGGESTIONS FOR GARDENING WITH CHILDREN

- Keep it simple, and start small. Plots that seem small at first will allow you and your group to experiment without being overwhelmed by season-long maintenance. You can always make the garden larger next year.

- Allow children as much ownership as possible in establishing their garden and choosing varieties of plants to grow. However, do get involved in the process. Not everything grows in all locations, and your group may need some guidance in selecting plants.

- It's okay to be messy! If you plan garden maintenance on regular days each week, parents can be notified ahead of time so students can dress for outdoor/dirty work.

- The garden doesn't have to be perfect. Not all gardens have straight, weed-free rows of tidy vegetables. Keep up with maintenance as much as possible, but allow children freedom to design their garden spaces.

- When planting, include plants for both immediate and delayed gratification. Transplants and quick-sprouting seeds like radishes and sunflowers will provide something to look at right away while waiting for slower seeds to sprout.

- Excite the childrens' senses by including visual and tactile plants. Plant brightly colored flowers that lead to beautiful, fragrant fruits, as well as "touchy-feely" plants–those that give off fragrances when they are touched or that have interesting textures to feel.

- Avoid poisonous and/or thorny plants. Research plants, or check with your local nursery, to make sure you don't introduce any hidden harmful plants.

- Encourage exploration and take advantage of "teachable moments" that crop up. There are many exciting things for your group to discover in the garden when everyone takes time to look closely and observe. Gardens are constantly changing as plants grow, bloom, and produce fruit.

- Don't be afraid to experiment. Even a dying plant can be turned into an investigation of what happened, rather than a failed venture. It's good for children to know that adults don't have all the answers, and you will be modeling science process skills for your group.

- Be flexible and have fun!

Basic Gardening

Groups with no previous gardening experience should complete several of the following basic gardening activities. Remember to consider time constraints and available resources. Your county Extension office may be a valuable resource to assist your group in learning the most time-saving and cost-effective means of growing nutritious fruits and vegetables.

Because they have grown the produce themselves, young gardeners are more likely to eat new and different fruits and vegetables. This sampling of produce will increase their nutritional intake. A fun-filled, hands-on garden provides an environment for youths to grow, harvest and try new and different foods.

Nutrition begins in the garden. The origin of almost any food can be traced back to the foods in the first three sections of MyPyramid, and they are all derived from plants. They are the grains, vegetables, and fruits groups. Also, most of our sources of meat are from animals that consume plants. MyPyramid divides food into six classifications or groups and shows the recommended daily servings for each food group. The foods that should be eaten the most are in the groups in the largest slices of the pyramid. Because so much our diet is plant-derived, it's important to understand basic plant life concepts. This understanding will help your gardeners raise healthy plants full of nutrients.

Young gardeners will learn how to garden for optimum plant growth, production and food quality.

ACTIVITIES

P. L. A. N.T. Needs, Small and Large, Rules 'n Tools, Touchy-feely Pies and Shake, Rattle and Roll, Who Goes There?

HELPFUL BACKGROUND INFORMATION

The Garden Journal Page (Appendix B, page 116-117) is a worksheet that gardeners can use to document various gardening experiences. They can record what's going on in the garden, how the garden looks, how the plants change, if the soil is dry, if the plants are having problems, if any insects are found, or anything else they want to write about. Gardeners can record these experiences weekly, biweekly, or as often as you like. Later, gardeners can add other worksheets to their Garden Journals, too.

PLANT CLASSIFICATION

Plants are classified into two major groups; angiosperm and gymnosperm. The difference between these two classifications lies in a plant's ability to produce true flowers.

- Gymnosperms, such as pine trees, lack true flowers and produce seeds in cones.
- Angiosperms, such as tomatoes and peaches, produce true flowers. Their seeds are found in their fruits. Most fruits and vegetables discussed in this curriculum do produce seed in their fruit.

PLANT STRUCTURES

The fruit is only one part of a plant that can be consumed. Roots, stems, leaves, shoots, flowers, fruits or seeds can be edible, though usually not all from the same plant. Going from the bottom of a plant to the top, examples of dietary plant parts include:

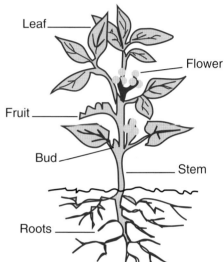

Roots: Carrot, turnip, sweet potato, radish, beet, parsnip
Stems: Celery and asparagus
Leaves: Parsley, basil, mustard greens, chard, spinach, lettuce, cabbage
Flowers: Broccoli and cauliflower
Fruits: Tomato, cucumber, pepper, squash, peach, apple, mango, kiwi, and apricot
Seeds: Pea, bean, corn, rice, barley, oat, nuts, sunflower and pumpkin

ROOTS

Roots are found below the soil surface and are essential to plants. There are two primary types of root systems: taproot and fibrous root. Taproots are one primary root with very few secondary roots and are found on plants such as carrots, beans and turnips. Fibrous roots are the many roots of similar size found on plants such as lettuce, broccoli, spinach and tomato. Tiny root hairs located on roots take up water and other nutrients from the soil. Roots transport nutrients and water to other parts of the plant. They also anchor the plant and help protect it from blowing over in winds and rain. Healthy roots are plump and white; unhealthy roots cause plants to wither and die from lack of water and nutrients.

STEMS

Sometimes called the "backbone" of growth, stems help support the plant and transport water and nutrients. Two components found in stems the are xylem and phloem. The xylem channel transports water and minerals; the phloem channel carries food manufactured by the plant.

LEAVES

Leaves, the plant's "food factories," transform light energy into plant energy. Chloroplasts inside the leaves make this transformation by changing sunlight, carbon dioxide, water and chlorophyll into sugars/carbohydrates. An actively growing plant with no leaves is unable to live long because it's unable to make food. Leaves also allow transpiration to occur, which helps cool the plant and maintain plant processes.

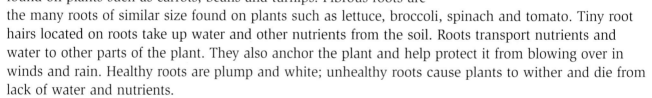

FLOWERS

Flowers are the showy part of the plant. Birds and insects are attracted to flowers and help transfer male pollen to the female pistil. Some flowers have male parts only; others have female parts only. These plants are called dioecious. Holly is one example. Other plants, like corn and squash, and most fruits and vegetables, have both male and female parts on the same flower, and are known as monecious. After pollination and fertilization have occurred, seeds develop.

SEEDS

Seeds can be spread by different methods, such as wind or birds, and have different mechanisms to help them disperse. After they settle into the soil, seeds germinate into new plants. Seed germination occurs when environmental conditions are favorable. Most seeds produced in the wild are different from either of their parent plants, much like children differ from their parents and siblings. Plants that consistently produce the same flowers or colors are sometimes referred to as "true to type." These plant varieties are available from local nurseries, markets and seed catalogs.

FRUITS

Fruits develop after the flowers have been fertilized. Most fruits and vegetables house their seeds in fruit, which helps protect and disperse them. The true definition of a fruit is "the seed-containing structure that is formed by the pollinated flower."

PRODUCING HEALTHY GARDENS

Most successful gardeners know what it takes to produce highly nutritious fruits and vegetables, and how to keep gardens producing until plants experience natural deaths. Plants have life cycles too, just like people. Most vegetable plants live one to two seasons, so they are called annuals (one season) or biennials (two seasons). Asparagus is an example of a perennial vegetable that is capable of living for years. Most fruit trees, such as peach and apple, and shrub/bush types like blueberry or blackberry are also perennials. Strawberries are considered herbaceous plants that are capable of living for more than one season; however, they usually are replanted each year in the South.

Most vegetables that you and your group will likely grow are annuals, and will need to be replanted each year. For easy reference, Spring and Fall Planting Guides, located in Appendix B, page 127, can help you determine which vegetables are appropriate for spring planting and fall planting.

A plant must be able to absorb nutrients and water from the soil. Different soils have different structures or water- and nutrient-holding abilities. Sandy soils allow water to run through the soil particles and are unable to store large amounts of water. Sandy soils need to be watered more frequently. Clay soils, on the other hand, hold water so tightly that plant roots are not able to extract it from the surrounding soil, even though water is present.

Most vegetable gardens grow best in a loam to sandy loam soil. Loam soils are made up of equal weights of clay, silt and sand, or approximately 20 percent clay, 40 percent silt, and 40 percent sand. Many soils can be enriched or amended by adding a 4-inch layer of compost and turning or mixing the compost into the existing soil. Amendments help improve the soil structure and increase moisture holding capacity, aeration and nutrient availability for plant use. Your county Extension agent will have more information on soils.

Teach your young gardeners to plant in the correct season, to use resistant varieties, and to practice safety and cleanliness measures. Leaf litter can be a haven for harmful fungi that overwinter in soil or dead plant materials and attack plants. It is important to dispose of or compost leaf litter on a routine basis, particularly after each planting cycle.

A bad gardening experience can be discouraging to youths and may inhibit them from attempting to garden again. Strive to give them positive experiences to share with other family members. More helpful gardening information is available in Appendix A, Garden Preparation and Planting Instructions.

P.L.A.N.T. Needs

Objective: To become familiar with the needs of plants and criteria for selecting a good garden site
Time: 50 minutes
Materials: Poster, markers, P.L.A.N.T. Needs worksheet (Appendix B, page 122), Site Selection Survey (Appendix B, page 123), pencils or pens, and clipboards if available

BEFORE THIS ACTIVITY

Plants need air, water, sunlight and nutrients to grow.

Air–Plants need carbon dioxide and oxygen from the air in order to perform important processes.

Water–Sometimes referred to as the "forgotten nutrient," water is important for all living organisms. The human body is more than 70 percent water; plants contain 80 to 95 percent water.
Function: In humans, water aids in digestion, lubricates bones and joints, regulates internal (body) temperature.
Plant Source: Includes all fresh fruits and vegetables.
Plants take up nutrients through water from the soil. Water also helps keep plants cool through a process called evapotranspiration.

Sunlight–Photosynthesis is the conversion of energy from the sun into plant energy. A plant cannot produce its own food without sunlight.

Nutrients–There are two types of nutrients: macronutrients and micronutrients. Macronutrients are needed in larger amounts and include nitrogen, phosphorus, potassium, magnesium, calcium and sulfur. Micronutrients are needed in smaller amounts; examples include iron, manganese, copper, zinc, boron, molybdenum and chlorine. Good soils contain these nutrients but poor soils may be lacking in one or more of the essential elements. Nutrients can be added to the soil by adding synthetic fertilizers (solid or liquid), compost (decayed plant materials) or mineral additives (lime or sulfur).

Your local county Extension agent can help you in preparing a soil sample to learn about the specific composition of your garden soil.

LET THE FUN BEGIN!

Indoors: Before going to the garden, begin a discussion of what people need to live. On a poster or chalkboard list five basic needs that all people share: food, water, air, shelter and clothing. Ask a student to circle the items that they think plants must have to be able to live. Ask if they know of anything that plants need that people do not. On the left side of a poster, vertically write the word "P-L-A-N-T-S" and tell students that everything a plant needs is found in that word. Complete the chart as shown below and have gardeners complete the P-L-A-N-T-S Needs worksheet (Appendix B, page 122) to add to their Garden Journals, or challenge learners to recall the list of plant needs without looking at the list.

P Place – in a container or garden for roots to grow
L Light – sun or artificial light
A Air – oxygen and carbon dioxide
N Nutrients – nitrogen, phosphorus, potassium and others
T Thirst – plants, like all living things, need water
S Soil – to grow roots in

DISCUSSION QUESTIONS

1. Can you recall all of the plant needs? Write them in your Garden Journal, using the word P-L-A-N-T-S to help you remember.
2. Where do plants get all of these things?
3. What do birds need, and how are their needs satisfied? Squirrels? People?
4. Which site did you decide would be the most suitable for your group garden? Why?
5. Did everyone in the group approve of using the same site?
6. What were some of the other students' reasons for recommending other sites?

Have students tell you what they like about their houses. Ask them what makes their houses comfortable places to live. With the word "P-L-A-N-T-S" still on the board, ask group members what kind of home they would build for a plant.

Now it's time to select the garden site. The leader may select the garden site if necessary, but allowing children to select the site can provide a valuable experience and ownership in the garden. If a garden area is already established, discussion can focus on the reasons the site was selected.

Outdoors: Take the group outside and stand in the shade of a tree. Ask group members if this would be a good spot to plant a garden. If possible, take them to a place near a ditch or where water stands and ask them what they think about that location. Next, walk to an area that is more isolated or distant from the work area and ask them if they think this location is a good spot. Discuss the pros and cons of each site. Ask the group to record these observations on their Site Selection Survey (Appendix B, page 123).

Remind students that the garden site should be sunny and easy to access, and the ground should drain fast and easily. Tell them that there are only two other things to think about: Is there a place nearby to get water? Is there a place to store garden tools and supplies?

Have three possible garden sites for students to consider. Ask them to rate each area using the Site Selection Survey.

When selecting a garden site, it is important to consider several items. A garden should:

- be easily accessible from the room where the group meets
- receive 6 to 8 hours of sunlight each day
- be located near a water source
- have loose and well-drained soil
- have tool storage space nearby

A garden site that meets all of these criteria will mean a more productive garden for your group.

In the Classroom

Have the students write a descriptive essay of their garden site that includes the P-L-A-N-T-S acronym. Each time they use a letter from the acronym, ask them to capitalize it so that each letter looks as if it will jump off the page. If students become stuck, write P.L.A.N.T.S. on the board and ask the class to repeat the meaning of the letters. Essay papers can be decorated and mounted on colored construction paper to hang on a wall, or have learners add their sheets to their Garden Journals.

Small and Large

Objective: To gain understanding of space considerations when planting seeds and transplants

Time: One 30-minute session and one 45-minute session

Materials: Seed paper towels, measuring tape, masking tape, graph paper, pencils, paper

After students have decided which seeds and transplants they will be planting, ask how they think the garden should be arranged. Ask what they think will happen if all the seeds are planted very close together. Use the P-L-A-N-T-S acronym from the previous activity to serve as a memory tag. If plants are planted too close, some might not get enough light or water. Tell gardeners that small plants, like radishes and carrots, can be planted closer together than larger plants, such as tomatoes or beans.

Ask four group members to volunteer to be radishes. Have them sit on the floor next to one another in a square and stretch out their arms and fingers as if they are growing toward the light. Ask six additional members to be tomato plants and stand closely around the radish plants so they are crowded. Have the tomatoes stretch their arms up and grow, too. The radishes should be feeling crowded at this point. Ask if they think they are getting enough light. Roots from the tomato plants will probably grow all around the radishes, soaking up water. Ask the rest of the class to suggest ways to rearrange the tomatoes and radishes so that they have enough space to grow, but not so much space that weeds are allowed room to grow.

Next, add a few more members to the plant group. The newest members are medium-sized spinach plants. Have the class decide on an appropriate arrangement and spacing for the plants. Ask them which side of the garden is the front side. Explain that gardens are arranged with consideration for visual appeal as well as vegetable spacing and shading. Usually gardens are planted in rows that run from east to west with taller plants at the back (northern rows), medium-height plants in the middle and shorter plants in the front (southern rows). Have them rearrange the plants one final time with these considerations in mind. Pose this question to gardeners, "What should you think about when you arrange plants in a garden?" Have them write their answers on paper that can later be added to Garden Journals.

Now, it's time for the gardeners to experience the garden. Take the group outside to the garden site. Have them measure its length and width. Return inside to recreate the space with masking tape on the classroom floor. (Hint: one standard-sized floor tile is 12 inches square.) Use the Paper Towel Gardening activity (Teaching Concept 2. Growing Techniques) to learn more about proper spacing for plants or refer to the Spring Planting and Fall Planting Guides (Appendix B, page 127-130).

Explain that they will be creating a "garden jigsaw puzzle." Divide the group into subgroups, working together, arrange the paper towels as they will be laid out in the garden. Reiterate the lesson: smaller plants grouped together toward the front, medium plants in the middle; and taller plants arranged along the back edge. After the layout is complete, make a map on paper to record the order and pattern of the paper towels. This map can then be used as a guide to plant the paper towel seed mats outdoors in the garden plot.

When planting the seeds outside in the garden, have youths practice their mapping skills by following the map they made in the classroom. One by one, have them place their paper towel seed mats in the garden and carefully cover them with a shallow layer of soil so the seeds are planted at the correct depth as specified in the Spring or Fall Planting Chart (Appendix B, page 127-130). (The planting depths will vary from $1/4$ inch to 1 inch, depending on the types of seed being planted. In general, seeds are planted twice as deep as they are wide. It is very important to plant seeds at the correct depth. If planted too deeply, seeds may not sprout.)

Have gardeners record their gardening experiences. Have them draw pictures to show their towels with the seeds on them and use their own words to tell how to make a paper towel seed mat.

In the Classroom

After the group has measured the garden area to find the number of feet on each side, have members use graph paper and sketch the garden area to scale. The easiest method is to make one paper towel square of garden space equal to one square on the graph paper. Then have members calculate the square footage of the garden, multiplying length times width, and include this on their garden area sheet too. Students can draw the shape of the garden on their paper then draw in the grid of each paper towel. They could create symbols to represent different plants and complete the garden map with a map key on the side to show which symbols go with which plants. Your group could also use a compass to find North and have the garden map include the cardinal directions.

Rules 'n' Tools

Objective: To establish rules for the garden that make it a safe place to learn and establish a schedule which allows all students take part in maintaining the garden

Time: 45 minutes

Materials: Poster board or construction paper, markers, pens and a monthly calendar

BEFORE THE ACTIVITY

Garden tools should be used only in the garden area, kept clean and safely stored after each use. Bacteria, viruses and fungi are easily transmitted to plants from dirty tools and hands. A practice of dipping garden tools and reusable containers in a 9-to-1 water-to-bleach solution helps reduce the transfer of plant diseases. Be sure to sanitize tools and containers that touch or come in contact with diseased plants or plant parts before reusing them.

To help keep tools from rusting and in good condition, apply a thin coat of an appropriate oil. Check with your local nursery or garden center and be sure to follow label directions.

LET THE FUN BEGIN!

As the garden is being developed, ask students to create a list of garden rules that will make the garden a safer place for the people working in it as well as for the plants. Brainstorm rules with the students. Pose the following situations to guide students in developing rules for their garden.

GARDEN SITUATIONS

- Someone is running through the garden and accidentally runs over and crushes a plant.
- A student is playing with a shovel by spinning it in the air and hits another person in the back.
- A student is walking on the timbers edging the garden, stumbles, and falls into some plants.
- The group arrives at the garden to find that the tools were left out all night. The wheel barrow has been stolen and some of the other tools are beginning to rust.
- A boy is pulling weeds and raking the soil. To pull a weed, he lays the rake down with the sharp tines pointed up. A girl walks by and steps on the rake. The tines stick into her sandal and cut her foot.
- A team is watering the garden. Members are talking to each other while the leader is telling them how much plant food to put in the watering can. They aren't listening and put too much plant food on the plants. Some of the plants die.

Try to keep the number of garden rules to fewer than seven. Have the class decide on the most important rules from their lists, and have students work with partners to make Garden Rules posters. Encourage students to make their posters colorful and to include illustrations.

DISCUSSION QUESTIONS

1. What happens if an adult breaks a rule like running a stop sign while driving?
2. Why do we have rules?
3. Do you think our garden would work as well if we had no rules?

We have talked about how to keep gardeners safe and healthy. Now let's discuss how to keep plants safe and healthy.

Ask who's thirsty. Explain that they have the ability to get up and get a drink of water. But how do garden plants "get a drink of water"? If it doesn't rain at the right time, plants need to have water brought to them by the gardeners. Your garden will need a water source that is easily accessible.

Hand-watering or using a soaker hose works well in small gardens. With hand-watering, half-gallon or gallon jugs can be filled at a sink or hose and carried back and forth to the garden. If the water has to be transported from inside or carried a long distance, use a cart or wagon to transport several jugs at a time. Show students how to slowly water at the base of the plant stem as they water plants one-by-one.

Soaker hoses are also effective means of irrigation. They are made of spongy, porous material that releases water slowly along the length of the hose. The hose can be laid alongside a row of plants, turned on, and left for a $1/2$ hour or longer. This allows water to soak into the soil thoroughly to a depth of several inches, and channels the water to the plants' roots, where it is needed most. (It also conserves water and avoids muddy messes!)

Discuss the garden's maintenance needs with students. Do they think that their plants need to be taken care of every day? Will their garden need to be watered and weeded every day? Explain that, even though the garden probably will not need care on a daily basis, it is a good idea to check plants often for signs of drying and for weeds.

Tell students that they are going to make a schedule that will ensure regular care of the garden by all students. Divide students into groups, and have each group come up with a group name. These groups will be the garden maintenance teams that take turns caring for the garden.

Show students a calendar that will be used as a master schedule. Prompt students to list tasks that are most needed: watering, feeding (fertilizing) and weeding. Tell them that the plants will need to be checked every other day for water. Have a student draw in a blue water drop on every Monday, Wednesday and Friday to signify a watering day. Next, have a member of each team come up and take turns writing their team's name by a watering day. That team will be responsible for watering on the days marked.

Mark one of the watering days each week as a fertilizer day as well. An easy way to fertilize is to use a water-soluble fertilizer. It can be easily spooned into jugs as students fill them with water. The plants will get fertilized as they are being hand-watered. (Note: If you use a granular fertilizer that is sprinkled onto the soil instead of a water-soluble fertilizer, it will not need to be applied every week. Read the label carefully and schedule fertilizer applications according to directions.)

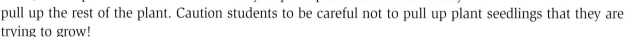

The last task to be added to the schedule is weeding. This needs to be done once or twice a week to keep weeds from taking over the garden. Explain that weeds steal the water, light and space that vegetables need. Decide on a symbol for weeding to put on the calendar and pick a day of the week to weed. Have groups sign up for weeding times. Demonstrate how to pull a weed, and explain that students should try to pull up a weed's roots as they pull up the rest of the plant. Caution students to be careful not to pull up plant seedlings that they are trying to grow!

Gardeners can keep records of what's happening in the garden in their Garden Journals using plain sheets of paper or predesigned worksheets. Ask them to record what's going on in the garden biweekly, weekly, or as often as you choose.

NOTE: The best way to check the need for watering is to stick a finger into the dirt approximately 1 inch (about the length from the tip of the finger to the first knuckle). If the soil feels dry at that depth, it needs to be watered. Deep, thorough watering is best for good plant health.

In the Classroom

Have the class use a calendar to answer the following questions:
How many months are in a year? Name them.
How many weeks are in a year?
How many days are in a year?
How many watering days are in a year?
How many weeding days are in a year?
How many fertilizing days are in a year?

Touchy–feely

Objective: To understand soil texture and the properties of different soil types and
particles
Time: 35 minutes
Materials: Three balls (three different sizes: basketball, baseball, nickel-sized rubber ball
or BB), flour, sugar or sand, water, poster, marker

LET THE FUN BEGIN!

Discuss with students some of the things they have learned about plant needs. What do they think will happen if a plant's roots are always dry or always sopping wet? To make sure that the roots of the plants stay healthy, you need to have good soil. On a sheet of poster board titled "SOIL–What's In It?," have students list what they think they would find in soil if they started digging. Write down all answers, even if not completely correct. The list will be modified later.

When the list is complete, discuss the ingredients in soil. One component of soil is small pieces of rock called particles. There are three main kinds of particles, and they are different sizes. The three kinds of soil particles are sand, silt and clay. Explain that sand is the largest particle. Show them the largest ball. The next smaller particle is silt. It is small. Show them the medium-sized ball. The smallest particle is clay. It is tiny. Show them the smallest ball. Use the balls to demonstrate the difference in the proportion of the particles to each other.

Sandy soil dries out quickly and does not let plant roots get enough water. Allow each student to feel the sugar, which is about the same size as sand, and have them describe it to you. Allow them to feel the dry flour and rub it between their fingers to understand the silky, powdery texture of silt.

Clay particles are very fine textured. They clump together and become slick and sticky. Soil that has mostly clay does not allow plants to grow well because there is very little air space between the tiny clay particles. Clay soils tend to be hard and compacted when dry, waterlogged (drain poorly) when wet, which makes it difficult for plant roots to grow. Let students feel flour with a little water mixed in to feel the slick texture of clay. You can also use wet cat litter to demonstrate this, because cat litter is composed mainly of clay.

Explain that the best soil for gardening contains a mixture of all three particles, with a small amount of clay. Add the three soil particles to the soil ingredient poster created earlier.

Have students describe what each type of soil particle feels like and include this page in their Garden Journals. The words Clay, Silt and Sand can be listed one after another, leaving enough room for young gardeners to write beside each kind of soil particle. Have them write the name of the soil particle that is the largest.

In the Classroom

Have the class try to grow seeds in different types of soils to see how plants respond. Explain that when they do this experiment, the soil type is the only component of the experiment that differs. All other components remain the same. The part of the experiment that is varied is called the variable. Everything that is the same (the kind of seed, size of container, amount of water, light) is called constants. By keeping constants the same, scientists can measure the change caused by the variable.

Students can conduct additional experiments using other things as their variables, such as different colors of light, different types of plant food, or anything else. Let students practice planning experiments to make sure that they understand the concept of variables and constants.

Pies and Shake, Rattle and Roll

Objective: To determine the soil texture and identify the amount of soil particles that make up a soil's texture

Time: 20 minutes

Materials: Jar, soil, water, waterproof markers

LET THE FUN BEGIN!

The previous activity, "Touchy-Feely," introduced the three types of soil particles. Use this as a way to introduce or review the components of soil.

Tell students they are going to make mud pies to determine if the garden soil has good texture. Ask them to help you dig a hole in the area which the group has chosen to use for their garden. Take enough soil so everyone will have a handful. Scrapping the soil off the surface will not give gardeners a true sample of their garden's soil texture. Rather, dig the hole at least 6 inches down into the soil. Mix the sample together well. Add a little water to the soil and make a mud pie. (Add just enough water for the soil to stick together. It should not ooze through your fingers but should make a good mud ball.)

Have the gardeners make an educated guess about the soil's texture. If the mud pie is crumbly and falls completely apart, the soil has a sandy texture. If it's sticky, glistens and keeps its shape, it's a clay soil. If the ball is loose, crumbly and not sticky, the soil is a loam soil.

Tell the gardeners it's now time to determine if their guesses are right! Use some of the remaining soil to fill a large jar half full, then fill with water. Have the gardeners take turns shaking the jar for several minutes until the larger clumps are broken apart. Let the jar sit for 2 minutes. Use a permanent marker to draw a line to mark the level of settled soil. Remind gardeners that sand makes up the heaviest particles, so it sinks to the bottom the quickest. Allow at least 24 hours without moving the jar for the mixture to settle further. The top layer will be clay, which includes the smallest, lightest particles. The middle layer will be silt, and the bottom will be sand. Have the gardeners decide which layer is the thickest to determine the soil's texture.

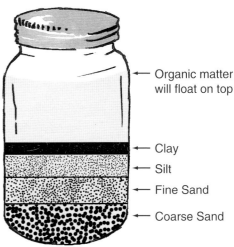

Organic matter will float on top

Clay

Silt

Fine Sand

Coarse Sand

Ask gardeners to compare their initial determination with the results of this soil test. Were they right? Which texture is best for their garden? Why is this? Vegetables grow best in a loam soil. If the garden soil is sand or clay, adding compost to it helps the soil retain moisture and replenishes nutrients for plant use.

AS AN EXTENSION

Have each gardener write a story about making mud pies: Include materials used (soil, water, jar); texture of the pie (smooth, grainy); color of the soil (light brown, dark brown); and any other information. Each gardener should include the story in their Garden Journal.

Who Goes There?

Objective: To learn the basics of Integrated Pest Management (IPM), and create a classroom IPM charting system

Time: 1 hour, plus 15 minutes for pest checks two times per week

Materials: Paper and pencils, Who Goes There? (Appendix B, page 124-125)

Before You Begin

Another factor in garden success is the control of damaging insects and pathogens in the garden. Less than 5 percent of all insects are considered "pests" that cause harm or damage to plants. Ninety-five (95) percent or more of insects are considered either harmless or beneficial. "Beneficials" are encouraged to visit the garden because they prey on damaging insects and help to keep gardens healthy and productive. See the photo keys (page 17-18) to help you identify more common garden pests and beneficials.

What is IPM? Integrated Pest Management, or IPM, is an effective way to address pest problems. Rather than applying chemical pesticides on a routine schedule, people who practice IPM use pesticides only when and where they find unacceptable numbers of pests. They try to control pests while not disrupting natural controls, such as beneficial organisms. An IPM program does not aim to eliminate pests totally, but rather to keep the number of pests below levels at which they cause too much damage (this is called the injury threshold).

Make treatments only after following these steps:
1. Gather and study information about the site, plants, potential pests and problems.
2. Monitor or observe the site and plants regularly to spot pests or problems early.
3. As soon as a problem occurs, establish an injury threshold. If you see that the damage reaches that threshold, take action to control the pest using the least toxic treatment first.
4. Keep good records, so you can base your future decisions and treatments on previous experience.
5. Evaluate each treatment on its effectiveness, and record any side effects.

The various ways that gardeners treat a pest problem are the "integrated" part of IPM, which has six basic strategies:
1. Choose plants that resist pests, support natural predators and encourage diversity. Make sure the plants and the garden design are appropriate for the climate, soil conditions, available resources and available maintenance levels.
2. Modify the habitat to discourage pests from living or feeding there and/or to encourage natural predators, parasites, diseases or competitors of those pests.
3. Change your practices and attitudes if they don't work. Change your cultural practices, such as mowing, fertilizing, watering, etc., if they cause problems. Also evaluate your attitudes about the need for "perfect" fruits and vegetables, manicured landscapes and total elimination of pests.
4. Use biological controls against pests. This includes creating an environment that helps existing natural predators, as well as adding to the population by periodically releasing natural predators.

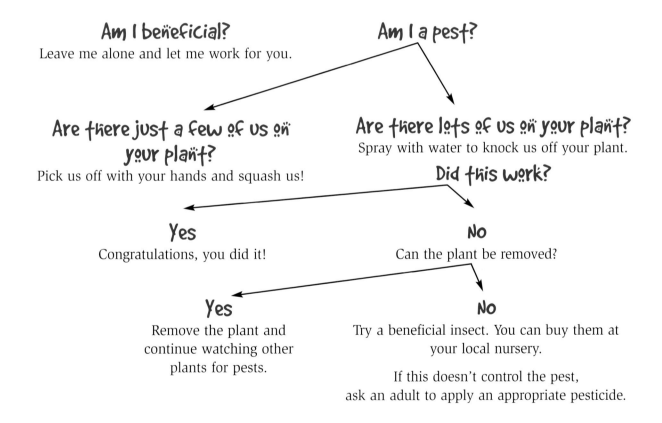

5. Physically control small populations of some insect, disease and weed pests through handpicking, barriers, traps, water sprays and dry conditions.

6. If you use chemical controls, emphasize those of an organic origin. There are scents that lure, repel and confuse pests; hormones that either stop pests from developing or act as contraceptives; fumigants and poisons that kill either on contact or after eaten. You also can use any combination of these controls.

LET THE FUN BEGIN!

Your gardeners must manage pests in the garden because it makes a big difference in how well the garden grows and produces. A garden pest is an insect that does harm to plant leaves, stems, roots, flowers and fruits in the garden. Gardeners and professionals use a method of managing pests called IPM, which stands for Integrated Pest Management. IPM discourages pests in a way that is environmentally friendly.

Gardeners can follow a simplified version of IPM by using the chart below. Help them follow the steps of the flow chart to manage pest outbreaks in their garden.

Am I beneficial?
Leave me alone and let me work for you.

Am I a pest?

Are there just a few of us on your plant?
Pick us off with your hands and squash us!

Are there lots of us on your plant?
Spray with water to knock us off your plant.

Did this work?

Yes
Congratulations, you did it!

No
Can the plant be removed?

Yes
Remove the plant and continue watching other plants for pests.

No
Try a beneficial insect. You can buy them at your local nursery.

If this doesn't control the pest, ask an adult to apply an appropriate pesticide.

Ask gardeners to scout in the garden each week to see what types of insects or signs of insect damage they see. For each insect, have the gardeners draw the garden pest they found and follow the IPM steps on the Who Goes There? worksheet (Appendix B, page 124-125) to determine which action, if any, needs to be taken.

Gardeners can choose to create a book containing these pages for future use. Have your gardeners create an ongoing list of Organism Observations where they can record the insect types they see in their garden, the plants these insects inhabit, if they are a pest or a beneficial, what type of damage or benefit the insect creates, and what action was taken, if any, using the Who Goes There? handout as a guide. (This could also be done individually by members of your group as journal entries.) Have gardeners do this activity for several weeks and include the worksheet pages in their Garden Journals. It is best to do this on an ongoing basis as part of the group's regular garden maintenance duty.

TOP TEN BENEFICIALS

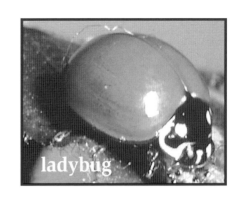

ladybug

praying mantis

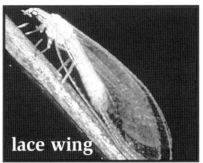

lace wing

Braconid wasp eggs on back of tomato hornworm

butterfly

bee

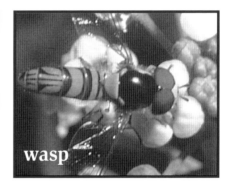

wasp

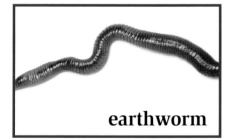

earthworm

pill bug

dung beetle

TOP TEN GARDEN PESTS

corn earworm

aphids

tomato hornworm

spider mites

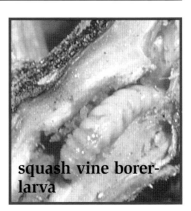

squash vine borer-larva

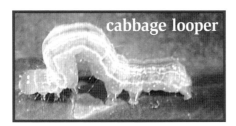

cabbage looper

cucumber beetle

squash vine borer-adult

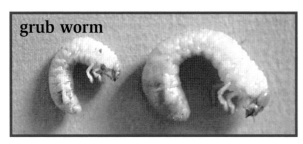

grub worm

mealybugs

Teaching Concept 2
Growing Techniques

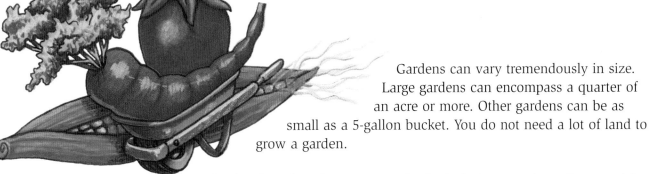

Gardens can vary tremendously in size. Large gardens can encompass a quarter of an acre or more. Other gardens can be as small as a 5-gallon bucket. You do not need a lot of land to grow a garden.

As the size of gardens vary, so do the techniques and practices used in them. Gardeners can learn different ways to help plants grow greener and healthier, depending on if the plants are in a raised bed, in the ground or planted in containers.

Young gardeners will learn different methods used by experienced gardeners and professionals.

ACTIVITIES

Paper Pots, Paper Towel Gardening, Make Your Pick, Protection by Diversity
Cylinder Gardening, Sack of Potatoes, Bean Tepee

PLANT LIFE CYCLE

A plant germinates, grows, flowers, produces seed and then dies. The length of each stage varies, depending on the type of plant. Within this life cycle, a plant passes through processes of pollination, fertilization, germination, photosynthesis, respiration and transpiration.

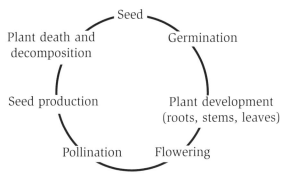

Seed → Germination → Plant development (roots, stems, leaves) → Flowering → Pollination → Seed production → Plant death and decomposition → Seed

Pollination: Pollen from the male flower is transferred to the ovary of the female flower.
Fertilization: Pollen is received by the egg; they unite to become a seed.
Germination: The seed begins to grow and becomes a plant.
Photosynthesis: Light energy is converted into plant energy (sugars/carbohydrates).
Respiration: Sugars/carbohydrates are broken down and used in plant growth.

Transpiration: Evaporation of water through stems and leaves occurs through small openings in the leaves called stomates. This helps plants maintain internal temperatures and absorb water and minerals from the soil.

Plants are unique:

- they have the ability to make their own food (autotrophic)
- plant cells have the ability to change and become something different (differentiation)

PLANT PROPAGATION

Gardeners have two ways to produce new plants: One way is through seed propagation (sexual propagation). Another method is through vegetative propagaton (asexual propagation) such as with cuttings, layering, division and tissue culture.

The simplest and most cost-effective way to produce more plants is by planting seed. A live seed needs the right conditions in order to germinate. But providing the right conditions does not guarantee seed germination. Seeds have a dormancy period or resting period that must be satisfied before they can germinate. Think of it as nature's way of protecting itself. Some seeds germinate easily; others have a hard seed coat that can take years to break down unless they have help from an outside source (called scarification), such as a bird's digestive tract. And still others need a chilling period (stratification) before they will germinate.

SOIL ADDITIVES

You many want to improve your garden soil by adding soil amendments, such as fertilizer on compost, to help plants grow strong and healthy.

Legumes are sometimes referred to as "green" fertilizers and are a special group of plants that help return nitrogen to the soil. Legumes include plants such as pea, clover and beans. A type of bacteria, called rhizobium, grows on the roots of most legumes and forms a mutually beneficial (symbiotic) relationship with the plant. The rhizobium takes nitrogen from the air and fixes it in the soil as a form of nitrogen that plants can take up and use. In exchange, plants provide carbohydrates (or sugars) to the bacteria.

Legumes can be planted as cover crops that cover the entire garden surface area when the garden is not in use. The plants are allowed to grow until they begin to flower; then the tops of the plants, including stems and flowers, are cut off and used elsewhere, while the roots are left to be tilled into the soil to decompose. After the plant roots have decomposed, the soil is replenished with a good source of nitrogen for plant use.

COMPOST

Compost is made of the following:

Green stuff: Any plant material that is still green adds nitrogen to the composting material. As the green stuff breaks down, heat is released and that speeds up the composting process.

Brown stuff: This plant material, which has been dead long enough to turn brown, adds carbon to the composting material.

Water: Water is essential to the composting process. Moisture allows fungi, bacteria and other creatures, such as pill bugs and earthworms, to break down the material.

Soil: Soils naturally contain living organisms that eat the organic material to make the composting process take place. Add a thin layer of soil occasionally throughout the composting process to distribute these organisms within the organic matter.

Air: Compost needs air to complete the process. The compost material must be turned regularly to move air throughout.

A compost bin can be made of wood, plastic, cement blocks or other materials available from nursery and garden centers. Locate the bin in any convenient, out-of-the-way designated outdoor area. Line the bottom of the bin with twigs and sticks piled upon one another to a height of 12 inches. This provides much needed air to the compost pile.

If using manure in the compost pile, be sure the composting process is complete before using the compost. Some food-borne diseases can be transmitted from partially composted manure. Ensure that the compost has generated enough heat to allow beneficial organisms to break down the pile and reduce the likelihood of transmitting and perpetuating food pathogens. To learn more about composting, contact your local Extension office or visit with a Master Composter.

Types and Styles of Gardens: What kind of garden will work best?

The type or style of garden that you use will depend upon your site. No matter what kind of site or space restrictions you have, you have gardening options! Let's look at two types of gardens: raised bed gardens (in the ground) and container gardens.

Raised bed gardens

These are traditional in-the-ground garden plots, with landscape edging around the perimeter that raises the level of the garden bed at least 8 inches above the surrounding soil. The soil inside the bed is prepared by digging and aerating the soil, the deeper the better, and raising the level of the soil by adding garden loam or topsoil enriched with organic material such as compost or composted manure. You can also fill the raised bed completely with garden loam or topsoil and organic matter, and not dig into the ground surface at all. This is a good option if your soil has poor drainage or is very hard, clayey or rocky. Raised beds improve the drainage of the garden, which results in healthier plants. The edging can be built up with any material that won't break down quickly, such as landscape timbers or natural stone. Make sure to stabilize the edging securely so it doesn't shift, fall and become a safety hazard.

Note: There is some controversy that chemical leaching from pressure-treated lumber, such as landscape timbers or railroad ties, can be a problem. Tests at Texas A&M University have not detected significant uptake by plants. Still some people prefer to use untreated lumber products such as cedar or redwood, or options such as natural stones or a gardening technique other than raised beds, such as cylinder gardening.

Square-Foot Gardening

This is a special raised-bed technique for growing crops intensively. It uses a grid system to plot plant spacing. Although it was developed with the primary purpose of maximizing the amount of produce grown per square foot of garden, many teachers have adopted it because the grid system lends itself well to math applications. Check out the book *Square Foot Gardening* by Mel Bartholomew.

Container Gardening

This uses containers instead of garden beds in the ground. You can use containers in small spaces and on cement- or asphalt-covered spaces where in-the-ground gardens are not possible. Containers are available in every shape and size, including whiskey barrels, wood, plastic or terra cotta planters, and window boxes. You also can improvise and use whatever materials you can obtain locally, such as buckets, tires or pallets nailed together. Anything goes!

Containers are easier to prepare than garden beds, because the digging is eliminated. Simply fill the container with potting soil, leaving an inch of space at the top for watering, and plant.

Note: Do not fill containers with soil taken directly from the ground. Soil that is well-drained and porous in the ground becomes compacted and rock hard when it is put in a container and watered. This is because the air spaces between soil particles form capillary tunnels that, along with gravity, aid drainage. In a container, these capillary tunnels are broken down, and water is not pulled down by gravity as it is in the soil. (It is, however, an interesting experiment to compare soil drainage in containers using soil and potting mix, and to have students hypothesize about the reason for the differences.)

Additional information on gardening techniques can be found in Appendix A, Garden Preparation and Planting Instructions.

Paper Pots

Objective: To create pots from recycled material in which to propagate plants from seed
Time: Day 1: 20 minutes, Day 2: 15 minutes, Day 3: 10 minutes
Materials: Newspaper, tub, plastic cups, pencil, soil, seeds, Paper Pot Transplants worksheet (Appendix B, page 126)

Before the Lesson: Choosing Seeds

Choosing the right seeds for your group to grow can enhance the learning experience. Remember, different plant species begin growing (germinate) at different rates. Some take much longer than others. Some types of seed can require light or dark conditions in order to germinate. Others must be kept at certain temperatures for a period of time. Before you pick seed varieties, determine how much time you have and where your garden will be located. Seed packets usually include the germination time and germination conditions. And remember, not every seed planted will germinate.

To protect itself, the seed has a built-in mechanism that allows it to rest and keeps it from sprouting for a certain period of time. This resting period is called "dormancy." Conditions may be picture perfect for growth but germination will not occur. When using seed saved from the previous season, allow time for dormancy to be broken.

BUYING TRANSPLANTS

Using transplants–very young, small plants–is one way to speed up the gardening process. You don't have to wait for seeds to germinate. Choose healthy plants when buying transplants from the nursery or garden center. A weak transplant produces a weak mature plant and will waste gardeners' time, energy, garden space and money.

Some transplants can be rootbound; they have roots that have formed a solid white mat around the inside and outside of the container. If donated or discounted rootbound transplants are used, you will need to cut those roots outside the container to free the plants. Then, take each transplant from its container and gently slice the roots vertically in four equally distanced places. This will allow new roots to form and grow out into the soil once the plant has been planted into its permanent home. A good rule of thumb is to never remove more than one-third of the root system.

LET THE FUN BEGIN!

Before beginning the activity, have students shred several newspapers into small pieces (about the size of business cards) and allow the paper to soak in a tub of water overnight.

DAY 1

Have students blend the paper/water mixture several minutes by hand until the paper pulp has the consistency of oatmeal. Take a handful of the mixture and drop it into a plastic cup. Allow students to shape the mixture by pressing it against the inside bottom and edges of the plastic cup. Tilt the cup so that the water drains as it is pressed out of the mixture. Use a pencil to make a drainage hole in the bottom of the paper pulp. Let dry for a few days in a warm place such as the window sill. Students can then pop the paper pots out of the plastic cups. (The plastic cups can be used again.)

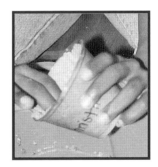

DAY 2

After the paper pots are dry, they are ready to be filled with potting soil. Explain to students that they will be planting seeds in the paper pots to raise their own transplants, similar to transplants that can be purchased from nurseries. Have students plant a few seeds in each of the paper pots. Use a planting depth of one to two times the diameter of the seed. Carefully cover the seed with soil, gently firm the top of the soil, and water each pot. Set the paper pots in a bright window, under a grow light, or in a greenhouse. Monitor them daily for progress and watering needs. When ready for planting, extra plants can be shared among the gardeners if someone's seeds do not sprout. Or students can take the extra plants home to plant in a container or home garden, or to give to a friend.

DAY 3

After the seeds have sprouted, let gardeners watch for the plants to produce two sets of true leaves. At this point, they are ready to be transplanted into the garden. The first leaflike structures that appear on a seedling are called cotyledons or seed leaves. They may be lumpy or strap-shaped and are usually a different shape and size from the normal leaves of the plant. Cotyledons are actually part of the seed that provide stored food reserves to the baby plant until it can establish roots and leaves with which to make its own food.

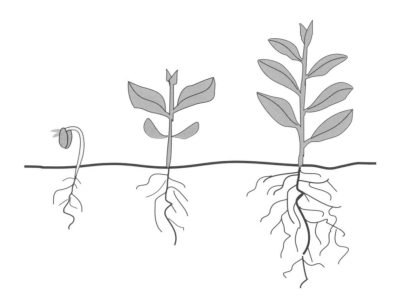

A week before transplanting, begin setting the pots of young plants outside for a few hours each day. Be sure to bring them indoors overnight. Lengthen the number of outdoor hours each day to allow transplants to become accustomed to outside conditions, temperatures and winds. This process is called hardening-off; it's a toughening up period for tender young plants.

Remember, not every seed will sprout and not every transplant will thrive. There will be "crop failures." Use the experiences as opportunities for gardeners to learn, even from mistakes. Turn what might otherwise seem a negative experience into a positive one by allowing gardeners time to think about what has happened and what might be done differently next time.

LATER IN THE GARDEN

The transplants can be planted in the garden or taken home by students. To plant transplants in the garden, use the following guidelines to ensure healthy, productive plant growth.

Explain that transplants are very fragile, so they will need to be handled very gently. (A young seedling is especially fragile. If crushed, the plant will not be able to transport water and nutrients from its roots to its leaves and the plant will die.)

There are just four steps in transplanting young seedlings into the garden. Take students out to the garden, and demonstrate the steps before they transplant their own plants.

1. Dig a hole. The hole should be about twice the size of the container. It is easier to work with the soil if it has been turned over, tilled or shaped into raised rows before planting.
2. If the transplant is in a plastic pot, remove the plant from its container. Do this by making a "V" with your fingers and thumb. Gently slide your fingers around the crown of the plant (place where the plant and soil meet) to form a cup around the top of the root ball. Turn the plant upside down with the top portion of the plant hanging freely between your index finger and thumb and hold onto the root ball in the palm of your hand. Gently tap the bottom of the container with your free hand to loosen and free the seedling from its container. If the transplant does not easily free itself, apply a little pressure, squeezing the very bottom of the container. Continue patting and squeezing the root ball loose until it comes out of the container.

   If the transplant is in a paper pot, you can leave the plant in the pot and put it directly into the soil. The paper pot will recycle into the soil.

3. Plant it. Plants should be planted at about the same depth in the soil as they were in their original container. The root ball should not stick up out of the soil, nor should it sink down into the soil so that the stem is buried. However, do cover the root ball with a shallow layer of soil, no more than an inch, to keep the root ball from being exposed to the air and drying out. Fill in around the roots with soil and gently firm the soil to remove air pockets.

4. Water it. Water the newly planted transplants using a gentle spray. A watering wand produces small water droplets and causes the least amount of damage to young seedlings. Thoroughly soak the topsoil several inches deep to allow the water to penetrate to the plant roots. (Demonstrate that a light sprinkle only dampens the surface and doesn't get to the roots where it is needed. Deep watering is important.)

Check the young transplants daily for the next 2 weeks to make sure they do not wilt or dry out. Have gardeners keep track of their seedling growth rates and harvest times in their Garden Journals. Compare this data to the crops that were direct-seeded or purchased as transplants.

As an Extension

Paper pots can be a good project for a fund-raising effort. The pots can be packaged and sold to parents and community members. Help the group plan the business of making and selling these recycled paper pots. Discuss the benefits of using recycled newspaper. Gardeners can have the experience of creating advertisements, packaging the pots, deciding a reasonable cost, handling money and selling their products.

In the Classroom

Have students write a "how-to" paper about making paper pots. They should use descriptive words to explain how to make paper pots. Each step should be included in the proper order. Learners also can use the Paper Pots Transplant worksheet (Appendix B, page 126) to draw a picture of what their plants look like when pulled out of the containers. Have them look closely at the roots and draw them, too. These experiences can be included in their Garden Journals.

Paper Towel Gardening

Objective: To create seed mats and transplant templates to help organize and lay out the garden

Time: 20 minutes

Materials: Paper towels that are about 1 foot square, seed, school glue, markers, masking tape, Spring and Fall Planting Charts (Appendix B, page 127-130), paper, colors, pencils

The directions that follow apply to seeds and transplants. If the gardeners are planting seeds, they can glue them directly to the paper towels. If they are planting transplants, they can use the paper towels as templates and mark spots or cut holes in the towels to show them where to plant in the garden later.

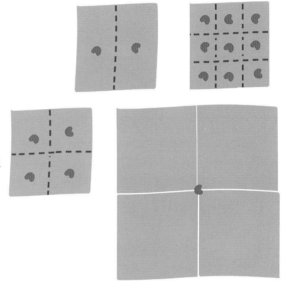

Team up the gardeners and give two paper towels to each pair. Help gardeners choose two plants to grow from their planting charts. Encourage them to choose one plant started by seed and one plant started by transplant. They will use the paper towels as spacing and layout guides when they plant in the garden. Have the partners write their names, the plant name, and the word short, medium or tall to describe the plant's height on each towel. Tell them they will plant their seed in a minigarden the size of the paper towel, and ask them how many plants can grow in that little space.

Ask the gardeners why they cannot grow many plants in a small space. What problems might the plants have? Have the gardeners locate their vegetable in the Planting Charts (Appendix B, page 127-130) and determine how many plants can be grown in the space the size of a single paper towel.

If the chart shows one seed per towel, the gardeners should paste a single seed (or make a mark) in the very center of the towel. If the chart shows four seeds per towel, the gardeners should fold their towels in quarters to make four equal sections. A seed can then be pasted in the middle of each of the four sections. If a plant calls for nine seeds per towel, the gardeners should fold the paper towel into thirds and then into thirds again, and paste a seed into the middle of each of the nine sections that result. (The children may have difficulty folding the towel into thirds, and may require some help.)

Explain that some seeds just don't germinate. It is a good idea to glue one or two extra seeds in each spot. If all the seeds do germinate, all but one plant can be removed. Explain that this is called THINNING. In this way, we choose the strongest looking plants to keep growing. When gardeners remove the extra plants, teach them to pinch off not pull each seedling at the base so the roots of others aren't disturbed.

Some plants, such as squash, grow large enough to require four squares or towels of space. Gardeners who choose crops that need this much space should tape four towels together to make a larger square (a full sheet of newspaper can be substituted for this large square) and then paste the seed in the center.

(Hint: Use paper tape, such as masking tape, and do not glue the seed directly over the tape.) If the garden space is small, limit the number of gardeners who choose plants that require four paper towels.

In the classroom

This would be a good activity to introduce fractions. Have the students fold a piece of paper in half and use a light colored crayon to shade one half. Ask them how many sections are on the piece of paper (two). Tell them to write the number 2 in the middle in each section. Now ask how many of those sections are colored (one). They should write the number 1 above the 2 in the colored section. Explain that this is called a fraction. The bottom number is how many pieces there are in all; the top number is the number of pieces you are talking about. Repeat the folding and coloring on other sheets to represent fourths, sixteenths, thirds and ninths. Have them write the fraction of each section on their folded papers.

Make Your Pick

Objective: To select appropriate vegetables for planting based on the season of the year
Time: 20 minutes
Materials: Fall and Spring Planting Charts (Appendix B, page 127-130), Make Your Pick journal sheets (Appendix B, page 131)

Before This Activity

Gather information about the planting dates for the vegetables listed in the Planting Chart (Appendix B, page 127-130) because planting dates of different vegetables can vary with location. You can also get information from your county Extension agent, seed packets, reference materials and the Internet.

Let The Fun Begin!

Ask the gardeners if they have ever eaten a slice of watermelon in December. In some areas, watermelons are available from the grocer all year long. Explain that when grown in the garden, some plants grow better at certain times of the year. Divide the gardeners into pairs and distribute copies of the Planting Charts.

Point out the column listing planting dates for each vegetable. Explain that the column under Recommended Planting Date is blank because planting times for each vegetable differ by region and state. Distribute the planting dates you have gathered and have gardeners fill in the boxes with planting dates for each vegetable. Have them cross out any vegetable with a planting date that occurs more than 2 weeks before or after the day you do this activity. Explain that planting these vegetables too early or too late may not leave enough time to produce a crop before the weather gets too cold or too hot. Some vegetables, such as lettuce and broccoli, tolerate cold temperatures better than others. These vegetables are better suited for fall and winter gardens. Vegetables that grow best in warm weather, such as watermelon and peppers, are better suited for spring and summer gardens.

Explain that gardeners may save money by growing vegetables (and other types of plants, too) at the right time of year and raising plants from seed or from already growing plants called transplants. It is best to use transplants if the planting date for seed for your region has already passed. This is especially true if planting seeds later than recommended for your area. Have pairs of gardeners select two crops from the planting chart, one planted by seed and one transplant (listed as a "T" under Planting Depth on the chart).

In the Classroom

Have each student research the vegetables he or she will plant. The students could use reference materials to learn about the crop (Veggie Research in the Appendix B, page 132) and make a collage about it. For example, the collage could include magazine pictures of the plant, its products, the season for best growth, which continent it's from, etc.

Your group can do a community service project to complement this activity. (See the Leadership/Community Service Projects on page 103.)

Protection by Diversity

Objective: To learn about diversity in the garden and its benefits
Time: 1 hour
Materials: Paper, pencils, graph paper, balls, tape, buckets

Ask gardeners to look to the right and then to the left. Who do they see? Ask them to describe each person using descriptive words.

Although we are alike in many ways, each one of us is different; we have a diverse population of people from different backgrounds and cultures from around the world. Different people have different strengths and talents. Real problems would occur if everyone had the same backgrounds, came from the same cultures, had the same talents and strengths.

How successful is a baseball team that can only hit home runs? Is the team with members with different strengths more successful? Diversity is important and encouraged in any group, team, club, school, town or an entire country.

Diversity is just as important for plants. Having different types of plants in an area helps to protect the plants against disease and insects. Disease can be caused by insects, fungi, bacteria or viruses that attack and enter living organisms. For a disease to successfully attack a plant, three things must be present:

1. a favorable environment (conditions for disease to survive and develop, such as the right temperature or humidity)

2. a weak plant

3. bacteria, fungi or virus.

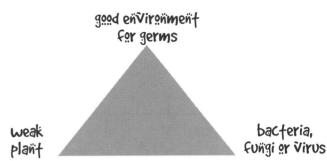

These components make up the Disease Triangle. If any one of these three parts is missing, a plant is less susceptible to disease. The best way to prevent disease is to keep the plant healthy.

In the 1980s, plant breeders learned the value of using plant diversity. A new and improved corn variety was developed. The next year, corn farmers planted all of their cornfields using only this new variety. However, they hadn't counted on a disease infecting and destroying most of the corn crop in the United States. If farmers also had planted other varieties of corn or planted a diversity of crops, such as beans, cucumbers, squash or pumpkin, this epidemic or devastating loss from disease might have been prevented. One reason plant epidemics occur is because large amounts of one single crop are planted; this is called a monoculture. Garden diversity, in large or small gardens, helps keep disease under control. A healthy plant eliminates the "weak plant" portion of the disease triangle and breaks the triangle. Reducing the chance of disease is healthier for plants and gardeners!

Ask the gardeners how each component in the Disease Triangle promotes plant disease. Follow by reviewing the list of good practices and ask them how each item affects the triangle.
Include as many of these practices as possible in the garden.

1. Make sure your plants are healthy when you buy them, and use plants well-suited for your area. (Your local nursery can help you select good plants.)

2. Check the tags that come with your plants or seeds. Space your plants just as the directions say. Overcrowded plants become thin and weak.

3. Layer mulch around your plants to prevent mud, which can carry fungus spores, from splashing up on your plants when you water.

4. Fertilize your plants regularly to keep them strong and healthy.

5. Be careful when you water. Avoid splashing water on the leaves.

6. Keep the garden clean. Don't let dead plants and weeds pile up (except in the compost pile). They can be a home for many pests.

7. Rotate crops each season. Planting crops in a different location of the garden each season helps to keep pests to a minimum. Some pests will attack only one type of plant or plants within a certain plant family. Rotate legumes (peas and beans) to help replenish nitrogen naturally in the soil.

LET THE FUN BEGIN! Make simple garden layouts for two consecutive seasons using the concepts of crop rotation and diversity discussed above. Draw the garden size, shape and scale on two pieces of graph paper. Orient the layout to the compass directions and show notable features such as the water source or garden shed. Remind gardeners to design with plant height in mind. The P.L.A.N.T.S. activity (page 4) can also help remind gardeners of plant needs. Read, display and discuss some companion plants, or Plant Pals (see table), to help gardeners plot each vegetable. The Plant Pals list can assist your group in creating a garden that has a diversity of crops. Discuss other ways to keep plants green and healthy. As a group, vote on the best designs to use in planting the next two seasons in the garden.

Plant Pals

Plant	Neighbor with:
Beans	Potatoes, carrots, cucumbers, cauliflower, cabbage, most herbs and vegetables
Beans, Bush	Potatoes, cucumbers, corn, celery, strawberries
Beans, Pole	Corn
Beets	Onions, kohlrabi
Cabbage	Potatoes, celery, onions
Carrots	Peas, leaf lettuce, onions, tomatoes
Celery	Tomatoes, bush beans, cucumbers, pumpkin, squash
Corn	Potatoes, peas, beans, cucumbers, squash, pumpkin
Cucumbers	Beans, corn, peas, radishes, sunflowers
Eggplant	Beans
Lettuce	Carrots, radishes, cucumbers, strawberries
Onion/Garlic	Strawberries, tomatoes, lettuce, beans
Peas	Carrots, radishes, corn, cucumbers, beans, herbs, most vegetables
Potatoes	Beans, corn, cabbage, marigold, eggplant
Pumpkin	Corn
Radish	Peas, nasturtium, lettuce, cucumbers
Soybeans	All vegetables
Spinach	Strawberries
Squash	Corn
Strawberry	Bush beans
Sunflowers	Cucumbers
Tomatoes	Onions, marigold, carrots

Growing Techniques

In the Classroom

Have gardeners learn teamwork through the following activity. First, discuss how all the parts (group members) are needed to do a task and how working together helps everyone get the job completed. Then, divide gardeners into teams of two. Blindfold one team member, and tape together the hands of the other member. Place buckets on the floor for each team or have teams share a bucket. The hands-taped gardener hands a ball or similar object to the blindfolded gardener. The blindfolded gardener then must walk and locate the bucket using verbal cues from his team member. Once the bucket is found, the blindfolded member drops the ball into the bucket. The ball must stay in the bucket for a team to complete the task. If not, the blindfolded member must find the ball and start the process again. The hands-taped member can only give verbal cues. He/she cannot touch the ball again after initially handing-off the ball. The fun is over when all teams have completed the task.

Cylinder Gardening

Objective: To learn how to successfully grow vegetables and herbs in containers
Time: 30 minutes
Materials: 5-gallon plastic buckets (can be obtained free from food or cleaning products), potting mix, seeds/transplants, fertilizer, brown paper bags or newspaper (four to five layers), Spring and Fall Planting Guides (Appendix B, page 127-130)

Before the Lesson

Cylinder Gardening uses 5-gallon buckets, which you can usually get free from cafeterias or restaurants, as minicontainers. Use a saw to cut out the bottom of a bucket and cut the bucket in half. The resulting two cylinders will make two minicontainer gardens. Simply place a cylinder on the ground and fill with potting soil. Each cylinder can be used as a personal garden plot for every one or two students. Extra cylinders can be used for theme minigardens or experiments. Cylinder gardens are convenient because they can be easily removed if needed. Just remove and compost the plants, remove and store the bucket cylinders, and spread out or compost the potting soil.

Cut the buckets into cylinders. Ask parents, Master Gardeners or other volunteers to help prepare the buckets. Have the volunteers remove handles from the buckets and cut off the bottoms (a bow saw or hand saw works well). The buckets should then be cut in half to create two cylinders of about 7 inches wide.

Purchase a commercial potting mix that is composed of peat moss, vermiculite and perlite. Add a slow release fertilizer (14-14-14) or use a water soluble fertilizer when planting. Follow directions on the label.

LET THE FUN BEGIN!

People who think they lack garden space can garden. There is always a way to garden, even in a parking lot! Share the cylinders with the gardeners and explain that cylinder gardening is a way to garden without the hard work of digging the soil.

Help gardeners locate an area that is flat and receives at least 6 to 8 hours of sunlight each day. Use 10 cylinders placed in two rows, 3 feet apart to allow for plant growth and enough room for gardeners to work. If the cylinders are placed on concrete, first lay the brown paper bags or newspaper on the ground and then set the cylinders on top of the paper. Have gardeners fill their cylinders with soil. Mix 3 tablespoons of slow release fertilizer into the soil of each cylinder. Then plant the seeds or transplants. Be sure that the gardeners monitor the cylinders to keep the soil moist. Cylinder-grown plants need more frequent watering than plants grown in normal garden soil. Refer to the information on the seed packets or use the planting guides (Appendix B, page 127-130) for more information on the correct season to plant. Gardeners also will need to check the plants for signs of insect damage and keep containers free of weeds.

In the Classroom

Discuss with your class different ways to experiment with variables using cylinder gardening. Remind them that a variable is a single thing done differently in one cylinder than in the others to determine if plants grow better because of the variable. Have learners decide which variable to study. Try using different amounts of soil, different types of soil, the addition of mulch, the use of slow-release fertilizer versus weekly water-soluble fertilizers. Explain that plant scientists conduct experiments using different variables to learn how to help plants grow better and stronger. Use more than one cylinder to test each variable.

Sack of Potatoes

Objective: To identify unique parts of a potato and grow potatoes in containers
Time: 2 to 3 months
Materials: *Oliver's Vegetables* by Vivian French, seed potatoes, potato with eyes sprouted, magnifying glass, Part of the Potato (Appendix B, page 133), knife, potting soil, plastic trash bags for the kitchen, water, iodine

Before this Activity

You can introduce the word "potato" to the group by reading the book *Oliver's Vegetables* by Vivian French to them. Discuss with the gardeners Oliver's difficulties in finding the potatoes. What makes potatoes so different from other vegetables?

Ask gardeners what has eyes but cannot see? (Potatoes) Display and allow gardeners to examine the seed potatoes carefully.

If possible, allow the gardeners to look at a seed potato under a magnifying glass. Ask them to write their observations on the Parts of the Potato sheet. They might use words or phrases like brown skin, dirt, scratches, knot areas, etc. Explain that the potato eyes are visible as small dimples on the potato surface. Each of these eyes is capable of sprouting a new stem. Show gardeners potatoes that have sprouted. Each small dimple, called a node, on the potato is the point where leaves attach to the stem. Show the nodes of a tomato or cucumber plant. Ask what part of the plant is the potato. They will be surprised to learn that potatoes are actually special stems, not roots, called tubers. Have the students find nodes on other plants.

Pass out the Parts of the Potato activity sheet (Appendix B, page 133). Allow the children to label the following parts of the potato on the worksheets: tuber, node, leaves, stems, and soil. Explain that potatoes are fun to grow and are healthful, too. Potatoes give our bodies carbohydrates for energy and are an excellent source of vitamin C.

Planting Potatoes

The tuber we plant is called a "seed potato." Although it's not actually a seed, it is called this because it is the part planted to grow a new plant. Use good seed potatoes, free of disease and chemicals, that are from a local nursery, garden center, seed catalog or plant supplier. Seed catalogs, local garden centers and the Internet can be used to locate seed potatoes. Do not use potatoes from the grocery store because these have been treated to prevent sprouting.

The seed potato supplies food for the young plant until it develops a root system. Small seed potatoes weighing 2 ounces or less can be used successfully when planted whole. Large spring potatoes should be cut into 1 $^1/_2$ - to 2-ounce pieces (about the size of a medium egg) with at least one good "eye" or node.

Cut the potato a few days before planting and allow it to heal over to prevent rotting when planted. One pound of seed potatoes will make nine to 10 seed pieces.

Place fall planting potatoes in a warm, damp location such as a shady spot under a moist layer of mulch for 2 weeks before planting. The potatoes will have small sprouts growing from the nodes at planting time.

Seed potatoes will be more readily available in the spring than the fall. You can choose to buy extra seed in the spring and hold it over until fall for planting. If so, keep the potatoes in a cool, humid place such as the bottom of a refrigerator. Because seed potatoes are living, breathing organisms, seed potatoes stored more than 1 year contain little or no food reserves to grow a fresh crop of potatoes.

As potatoes grow, pull soil media or thick mulch to the plants. Tubers form above the seed potato and those that form in soft mulch often produce smoother, better shaped potatoes than those grown in soil (especially if soil is heavy). As tubers (potatoes) form, protect them from sunlight. A green potato has been exposed to sunlight and this portion should not be eaten. Applying a thick layer of mulch when the plants are 8 to 10 inches tall will help reduce soil temperatures and increase yield and quality.

Use clean soil or a high quality soil-less media if growing potatoes in containers. If growing in the soil, practice a good rotation program to control soilborne potato diseases. Avoid planting potatoes in the same spot of the garden for 2 consecutive years. Avoid planting potatoes after eggplant, okra, pepper or tomato because they can be affected by the same soilborne diseases.

Harvesting/Storing Potatoes

Potatoes are ready to be harvested when the top leaves begin to yellow or the plant produces flowers.

Harvesting potatoes is like having a birthday. You never know what you're going to get. Harvest potatoes when the soil is moderately dry. Pull the potatoes gently from the vine and handle with care to prevent damage because damaged potatoes do not store well. Allow the potatoes to dry, then store in a cool (60 to 70 degrees F), moist spot with plenty of air movement for the next 3 months. This process is called "curing."

During this 3-month period, potatoes will not sprout even if planted in soil under ideal conditions. This is a self-protection mechanism to ensure survival. Store seed potatoes at 39 to 40 degrees F and 85 to 90 percent relative humidity (bottom of a refrigerator).

Nutritional Information

The average American eats more than 147 pounds of potatoes a year. Potatoes are a part of a well-balanced diet, providing carbohydrates for energy to the brain and muscles.

An average baked potato contains 220 calories and has almost no fat. Most of these calories are in the form of complex carbohydrates, also known as starch, and potatoes are a good source of vitamin C. Potatoes also are a source of fiber if you eat the skins.

Adding butter, sour cream, cheese and bacon to baked potatoes can add flavor but can add more than 340 additional calories and 40 grams of fat. Caution: Wash potatoes under running water and cut away any green portions of the potato before using.

LET THE FUN BEGIN!

The best time to grow potatoes is when the temperatures are cool. (In most areas, potatoes can be grown in the fall or spring.) A fun way to grow potatoes is in a trash bag! Use seed potatoes from a local nursery. Commercial potatoes are chemically treated to prevent sprouting and will not work as well. If needed, cut the seed potatoes into small pieces containing one or two eyes, approximately 1-inch to 2-inch cubes. This should be done a day or so ahead of time so that they can dry slightly to discourage disease growth.

Select a sunny location outside where you can grow your potatoes. Do your work in this permanent location because the finished product will be too heavy to move.

Fill a plastic kitchen trash bag about half full with potting soil mix or compost. Make a few holes with a pencil in the bottom of the bag so that water can drain out of the bag. Plant two or three seed pieces in the bag. Cover the seed pieces with additional potting soil or compost so that there is about a 2- to 3-inch layer of soil over the seed potato pieces. Then, water thoroughly.

When the plants are 8 to 10 inches tall, add more potting soil or compost under the leaves to the top of the bag, allowing the potato plants to continue to grow. Keep light from reaching the new baby potatoes. If light reaches the potatoes, the exposed potato portions will turn green and will not be good to eat. The seed pieces should now have about 6 to 8 inches of soil on top of them.

In about 10 to 12 weeks, split the bag by cutting it vertically down one side and then the other. Lift the plants from the bag and gently shake away the soil. You'll harvest some of nature's best energy machines. Potatoes!

Harvested potatoes should be stored in a cool dry place such as a cabinet.

Before cooking the potatoes, be sure to wash and scrub them thoroughly. Bake, mash or oven-roast them for a yummy dish. Save some of the potatoes to use later as seed potatoes, barter with them at a swap shop or share with other gardeners. Try making a red, white and blue potato salad to help celebrate Independence Day.

In the classroom

Can we test for the presence of starch (complex carbohydrates)? In chemistry, many substances change color when they react with other substances. An example of this is iodine. Iodine turns blue when it comes in contact with starch. This is a helpful indicator to test for starch—just add a drop of iodine. Try this test with things like potatoes, apples and other fruits and vegetables. Gardeners can make a table or graph as a visual display of all of the foods tested for starch.
Remember not to eat anything that you have tested with iodine!

Bean Tepee

Objective: To grow pole beans on a tepee style trellis that creates a livable space
Time: 2 months
Materials: Pole bean or pea seeds or transplants, six poles made of 10-foot lengths of bamboo, cedar, pvc pipe or lumber, twine or small rope, weather-proof cord or wire and Pole Race activity sheet (Appendix B, page 134).

Before the Lesson

Green beans are fruits picked from the plant before the seeds have reached maturity. Harvest green beans that have a slight ridge, which can be felt by running the pod between the fingers. At this stage, the beans are not bulging and are without strings when snapped in two.

Green beans are a tasty, nutritious and practically fat-free vegetable. A mere 22 calories per $^1/_2$-cup serving of green beans provides fiber and some vitamin C, along with other important nutrients. Including this vegetable in a healthful lunch or dinner is one way to reach the recommended goal of five servings of fruits and vegetables each day.

> **Vegetable function:** Helps keep the digestive tract clean and clear
> **Vegetable sources:** Snap beans, sugar snap peas

Beans and peas also can be harvested when the pods are very large and swollen. At this stage, the seeds inside the pod have fully developed or have reached maturity. Allow the seed pods to dry on the vine. Dry beans and peas are included in more than one part of MyPyramid. A $^1/_2$-cup serving of dry cooked beans can count as either a serving from the vegetable group OR as a 1-ounce serving from the meat group. Dry beans or dry peas are an economical source of protein, especially when eaten with a grain such as rice. Additionally, one serving of dry beans can contribute to more than 30 percent of the daily value of needed fiber, along with other important nutrients.

> **Functions of protein:** Builds body and repairs tissue; provides energy; regulates body functions; helps transport nutrients and oxygen
> **Protein plant sources:** Nuts, pinto, kidney, black beans, navy beans and peanut butter.

Ask, "From what is your house made?" Explain that some Native Americans lived in houses called "tepees" that were made from animal hides. They used horses to move their houses from place to place in order to follow the buffalo. Ask gardeners if they could use horses to move their houses. Lead them into a discussion of different materials to use to cover a tepee. Explain they are going to make a living tepee in which they can sit and play.

First, have your JMG group locate a space that is at least 6 feet by 6 feet in the garden, receives full sun and is close to a water source. Consider using an edge of the garden to allow gardeners easy access in and out of the tepee. A 1-foot wide border of stone, concrete or mulch surrounding the tepee will allow gardeners to weed and water their living tepee.

The next task is to select six, 10-foot poles made from bamboo, plastic pipe, cedar or pine wood. Tie and secure the poles together at a point 6 inches from the top with a weatherproof cord or wire; and place the base of the poles 1 foot to 2 feet apart to form a circle. Be sure to leave a 2-foot opening between the front poles to use as a doorway. String twine or a thin rope between and around the poles so the vines can climb around and to the top of the tepee.

Plant dry beans or peas to grow on the tepee. Be sure to use a climbing or "pole" variety.

Ask the gardeners to plant their bean seeds or transplants 1 inch from the base of each pole. Gardeners will need to train the plants to grow around and along the poles. Ask, "How do beans climb a pole?" They don't have arms and legs, but beans and peas do have "tendrils." These tendrils act like strong arms that wind around objects as the plant grows. They hold on so tight that even a strong wind can't blow down the plant.

Have the gardeners place a 4-inch layer of mulch around the base of the tepee. Explain that mulch helps the soil stay moist and cool. Plants with a layer of mulch need less water and weeding. Weeds compete with plants for water and nutrients in the soil.

Four to 6 weeks later, the plants will cover the tepee and fruit (flower) set will start. Gardeners can grow green beans or peas or dry beans. Discuss with gardeners the differences between green beans/peas and dry beans. Show them a green bean. Explain that green beans are fruits picked from the vine at the immature stage when they are green and before the seed pods swell. At this stage the pod is green and small with tiny seeds inside. Eating this vegetable as part of a well-balanced diet supplies the body with fiber and vitamin C.

Then show gardeners the dried beans or peas and ask how these beans are produced? Dry beans and peas are mature fruits because the seeds inside a pod have been allowed to fully develop and swell. These pods turn brown, dry on the vine and are harvested later. Show gardeners a whole, fully developed, swollen pod. Explain that green beans are the children and dry beans are the adults of bean/pea plants. Dry beans and peas give us protein and fiber; they act like scrub brushes inside the body and help to keep the body clean.

Be sure to practice food safety when storing the harvested beans/peas. Refer to Teaching Concept on Food Safety for additional information.

In the Classroom
Determine the percentage of seeds that germinate and the rate of growth for each seedling. Plant 10 or 20 seeds around each tepee to help students calculate the percentages. Have students plot and graph the daily or weekly growth of each seedling in centimeters or inches using the Pole Race activity sheet (Appendix B, page 134). Students can also calculate and graph the dates of flowering and dates they harvest green beans and/or dried beans.

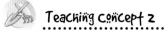

Thrifty Gardens

Gardening is fun and it can be economical, too! Gardeners can find ways to save money by growing their own fruits and vegetables at home or in community areas. The money saved from making fewer purchases at the grocery store can be used to buy that something special or be kept in a bank.

From a few seeds comes a ton of food. Gardens help extend the food budget and ensure quality nutritious foods over a period of time. Like many hobbies and business ventures, it takes time, money and energy to keep the garden growing, productive and beautiful. Help your young gardeners understand some cost benefits of gardening to produce foods that are healthful and nutrient packed. The work done in these activities by your group members can help them plan ahead and extend their resources.

Teach your gardeners to put their gardening resources to work to produce quality, nutritious foods for themselves and their community by using the following activities.

ACTIVITIES

Shop 'n Grow, Food Storage Gardens, Plan 10 in 2,
Seed Bank, Swap Shop Eats

HELPFUL BACKGROUND INFORMATION

A variety of fruits and vegetables are available year round as fresh and processed goods. Processed fruits and vegetables can be canned, frozen and dried. Fresh, quality produce from the garden is nutritious, economical and has great aroma and flavor. Gardeners should handle and preserve fresh fruits and vegetables in a correct and timely manner to get the most product for their time, energy and money. The work your gardeners do and the time they give to the garden will allow them to experience and understand that gardens, and money spent to maintain them, can produce quality foods over time.

What are the start-up costs associated with establishing a garden? Costs really depend on your location, soil type and gardening system. In most cases, the construction of a raised garden bed, measuring 8 feet by 4 feet using landscape timber and soil amendments such as compost, will cost an average of $250 including labor. Groups can save money by recruiting parents and community members to provide time and labor for construction of the garden. Starting with a small garden and increasing its size on a regular basis will involve young gardeners and give them an opportunity to help plan, design and plant the new garden area.

Help your gardeners learn to save money and the environment. Let them use plastic gallon milk jugs to make low cost gardening tools such as shovels, siphons, humidomes, etc.(Hint: Clean milk jugs with hot water and a mild dishwashing soap. For lingering smells, rinse the jugs with a weak bleach solution in a 9-to-1 ratio [nine parts water to one part bleach].)

Show gardeners how to use wooden pallets, which often are discarded by nurseries and garden centers, to make useful and inexpensive compost bins. Spent garden hoses can be cut up to make door handles or handles for 5-gallon buckets. Involve parents, grandparents, neighbors, master gardeners and other volunteers to assist in recycling timbers and lumber for use in your compost and gardening areas.

Challenge and encourage gardeners to recycle as many different plastic, metal and wood scraps as possible. Valuable landfill space is becoming more and more limited each year while associated costs continue to rise. Less trash at the curbside means less space used in landfills. Gardeners can learn about preserving the environment by reducing waste.

Food stamps are available to qualifying families and, depending on your area, may be used to purchase foods and some gardening supplies such as seeds, transplants or compost for use in food gardens. In an informal survey, very few store managers contacted knew that food stamps could be used to purchase gardening items to establish and grow food gardens. (Food gardens are garden areas that produce quality, nutritious vegetables, fruits, nuts and grains.) Check with your state to determine purchasing power and recipient qualifications for use of food stamps.

Sometimes, coupons can be used to save money. However, the use of coupons does not necessarily guarantee savings. Some retailers use advertisements in the form of store coupons to market a product, but in reality they are advertising the store, not discounting prices. It's a good practice to check the regular retail price and compare it to the coupon price before purchasing items.

Additional activities found in other chapters also can be used to support the food resource management skills presented in this chapter. They are: Paper Pots, page 22; Cylinder Gardening, page 31; Chip Strips, page 94; Symmetry Snacks II, page 90; Sack of Potatoes, page 33; Save It, page 58; Make Your Pick, page 27; and Fruit and Veggie Mania, page 79.

Shop 'n Grow

Objective: To learn and practice food resource management using a coupon system to obtain needed gardening supplies

Time: Ongoing

Materials: Gardening catalogs, coupons, food stamps, scissors, paper and pencils

Before This Activity

Check with your local county Extension office or State Department of Human Services to determine if food stamps can be used to purchase gardening supplies such as food-producing seed and transplants. Not all store operators are aware that food stamps may be used to purchase gardening items. Consider contacting your local grocery or garden supply store directly.

Let The Fun Begin!

Ask group members if they have ever shopped for something from a catalog. What did they want to buy? Explain that they are going to shop for gardening supplies needed for their garden. Give examples of items they might need to purchase (compost, fertilizer, transplants, seeds).

Follow by asking if their parents use coupons or food stamps when shopping. If so, what kinds of coupons do they use? Explain that coupons are like money. People use them to buy things such as books, toys and food at reduced prices. Explain that stamps used to buy food are called "food stamps." Food stamps help families stretch their food dollars. Ask gardeners if they think food stamps could be used to buy some of the supplies they will need for their garden, such as carrot seeds or tomato plants. Explain that food stamps also can be used to buy gardening items for their food gardens. Food gardens are used to grow fresh fruits and vegetables to eat or store for later use.

Divide the members into several small groups. Have each group make a list of items that will be needed for the garden. Follow this by making a master list of individual items. Create a list of characteristics of each of these items. For example, if a shovel is needed, consider how the shovel will be used. Not all shovels are alike. Some are short, some are long, some have a flat edge, some are rounded, and some dig postholes. Gardening supply catalogs and seed catalogs can help the gardeners determine their needs and make wise and informed choices.

Have the gardeners look through local newspaper inserts and magazines and cut out valid store and manufacturer coupons. These can give gardeners lessons on which businesses accept food stamps, and when and where to use cash to buy the supplies they'll need. Yard or garage sales often have quality tools available for very reasonable prices. Consider visiting a few one morning with your gardeners.

Field Trip

As a group, visit a store that accepts the collected coupons and/or food stamps. Encourage parents to participate in this activity. Ask them to assist the gardeners to shop and compare the prices for their needed garden items. Discuss and compare:

- the difference in price between manufacturers for similar items,
- the difference in price for different tools and supplies, i.e. shovels versus hand trowels,
- the difference between the sale price and the regular price.

DISCUSSION QUESTIONS

1. Which items need to be bought this time? (examples include soil-less mix, seed, transplants, etc.)

2. Which items can be used again? (examples include shovels, hand trowels, plastic pots, etc.)

3. How much money did you save using coupons?

4. What was bought using food stamps?

5. How much money did you save on purchased gardening items (i.e. hand trowels) that can be used again?

6. What could the group do with the money that is saved? (Encourage them to save at least 10 percent in a bank.)

FOOD STORAGE GARDENS

Objective:	To learn that gardening provides fruits and vegetables over time
Time:	Ongoing
Materials:	Journal sheets (Appendix B, page 116-117), Harvest Time Line (Appendix B, page 118), pencils

Have the gardeners call out plant parts–roots, stems, leaves, flowers, fruits, seeds. (Using this order gives gardeners a rhyme, making it easier for them to memorize.) Ask them to name the plant parts that people eat. Discuss the different fruits and vegetables and ask them to name which part of the plant each one is. Remind them that we eat all parts of plants.

Next ask the gardeners, "How long does a garden last? One week, 1 month, 1 year?" Ask them to guess how long each vegetable or fruit plant in their garden will keep producing food. Most fruits or edible portions reach their mature (harvest) stage over a period of time rather than all at once. Peaches on a tree usually reach the harvest stage (maturity) over a short period of time (from the time it takes the first peach to mature to the time it takes the last peach to mature is often less than 1 month). Pineapple plants generate only one pineapple from each plant and it can take more than 2 months to develop and mature. Ask the group how long vegetables such as lettuce or spinach will last in the garden. Explain that some greens such as lettuce and spinach can be harvested over a season as long as only the older (outer most) leaves are harvested and the weather remains cool.

Have gardeners create a Garden Journal using the pages in Appendix B (page 116-117). When they begin harvesting vegtables, ask them to bring their journals to the garden. Ask gardeners to begin writing the first date they collect ripe fruits and vegetables and each day thereafter. If gardeners begin harvesting tomatoes on June 1 and the tomatoes keep producing through most of September, then your gardeners will have a long list of dates and notes on the tomato page. Collections of different thoughts and observations made in their gardens, such as insects or insect damage they observe, can also be included. Expect, and explain to your group, that the journals most likely will get dirty and messy but it's "okay" since this is an acceptable part of gardening.

At the end of the growing season, have your gardeners transfer their harvest dates to the Harvest Time Line (see Appendix B, page 118). Each fruit or vegetable harvested will be depicted on a separate time line for easy reference. The tomato data collected earlier would be transferred to create a horizontal line that begins on June 1 and continues through most of September. Gardeners will become more aware of their plants, gain an overall idea of what's going on in their garden environment, and understand the amount of time a garden can be in production.

In the classroom

Have gardeners make a graph using the information found on the Harvest Time Line pages. All of the different harvest dates should appear in the graph. Total weights of produce also can be recorded and graphed. Ask gardeners to discuss and compare differences in the length of time fruits or vegetables are available. Which fruit or vegetable was available for the longest time and which was available for the shortest time? Compare differences in weight for each vegetable or fruit. Which weighed the most? Which weighed the least?

PLAN 10 IN 2

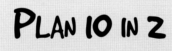

Objective: To learn meal planning on a budget, to include 10 servings of fruits and vegetables over a 2-day period

Time: 45 minutes

Materials: MyPyramid for Kids Poster (Appendix B, page 136), list of familiar fruits and vegetables, "10 in 2" (Appendix B, page 121) pencil, newspaper fliers and inserts or list of foods and prices

BEFORE THIS ACTIVITY

You can predetermine selection and price of foods to be used in this activity. Refer to the JMG Web site for a link to the Official USDA Food Plans: Cost of Food at Home at Four Levels. Give copies of this to gardeners and encourage them to use newspaper fliers and inserts to help them determine and calculate prices for foods in their menus.

LET THE FUN BEGIN!

This activity can be used in conjunction with the MyPyramid activity (see Teaching Concept 5). Ask the members what they would buy with $6 or another preset amount of money. Is the purchase something they need or something they want? Explain the difference between a need and a want. A want is something we'd like to have but do not need in order to stay alive. A need is something we must have–food, water, or shelter–in order to live.

Review a typical day at home or ask members to call out the previous day's activities, chores and duties. What items–television, dishwasher, sandwich, milk–were used? Ask members to decide whether each item mentioned meets a need or a want. Turn the discussion to the foods. If possible use the food items mentioned in the needs and wants discussion. Based on MyPyramid, determine what foods we need to stay healthy. Point out the fruit and vegetable section.

Explain that to help us grow up healthy and strong, it is recommended that people eat at least five servings of fruits and vegetables each day. It is more fun and healthy for people to eat a variety of fruits and vegetables than to eat the same ones day after day. Have small groups plan 2 days of well-balanced meals using the "10 in 2" activity (Appendix B, page 121). Give them these guidelines: use a budget to plan six meals (three per day) plus snacks (two per day). Encourage them to include as many different fruits and vegetables as possible, for a total of 10 servings during a 2-day period. Challenge gardeners to recall as many different fruits and vegetables as possible. Remind them of fruits and vegetables that are growing in the garden or that they have learned about in other activities. Your gardeners will benefit from looking at gardening catalogs or garden magazines to help plan their meals on a budget. Their other challenge is to stick to the budget of $6 or other preset amount. Encourage them to use as little of their budget as possible.

Explain that vegetables and fruits from their garden can help their families eat better plus save money for other things they need. Groups can calculate the cost of buying their fruits and vegetables and compare these costs to the cost of growing these items themselves. (Use seed, fertilizer, etc., purchased for this season's garden or that will need to be repurchased for the next garden. Do NOT include gardeners' time and energy.) Money that is saved through gardening can be used to stretch food dollars.

STORING LEFTOVERS

Cooked vegetables should be properly stored and used within 36 hours of preparation. Unused leftovers can be a waste of time, energy and food.

AS AN EXTENSION

Challenge gardeners to reuse the newspaper ads and grocery inserts from above to create a week of thrifty meals for their families using the plans available from the USDA Food Plans: cost of Food at Home at Four levels. These guidelines are just a click away when accessing the plan through the JMG Web page *www.jmgkids.us*. Have gardeners plan a week of meals for their family using one of the following plans: (1) a thrifty food plan, (2) a low-cost food plan or (3) a moderate-cost food plan. The budget allowable for each plan is calculated based on the family size and the age of each family member.

EXAMPLE OF A FOOD PLAN

Family Member	Thrifty Plan	Low-cost Plan	Moderate Plan
3-5 years old	$17.10	$21.30	$26.30
9-11 years old	$25.30	$32.10	$41.10
20-50 years old, female	$26.10	$32.50	$39.60
20-50 years old, male	$28.70	$37.20	$46.40

Calculate a weekly budget for a family of a mother, father and two children, ages 3 and 10. If following the thrifty plan, a gardener would use a food budget of $97.20 per week for this family. If using the low-cost plan, the gardener would allow a family food budget of $123.10 for the week and so on.

As gardeners plan their family meals, three meals for each day of the week, have them determine the number of servings a food source could provide. (The ABC's of Healthy Eating teaching concept has information on serving size and number of daily servings.) Would a family of four be able to get four servings from a can of green beans? If a box of cereal is purchased, how many breakfast servings could one box of cereal provide in a week's time? As the gardeners are creating their lists, they should be able to include reasonable amounts of different foods to provide adequate servings for all family members.

SEED BANK

Objective: To collect and save seeds from various fruits and vegetables to be used in the next planting

Time: Ongoing

Materials: Seeds from vegetables; paper towels; air-tight containers; Made by Nature envelopes (Appendix B, page 119-120); construction paper, glitter and other decorative materials; and glue.

One expense of gardening season after season is the purchase of plants and seeds. Your group can create its own "bank" of seeds. The seed bank can provide the group with a variety of seeds made by nature to use in home gardens or a group garden.

Tell the gardeners that they are going to begin a seed bank. Explain that a seed bank is like a regular bank–they can't just take seeds out, they also have to put seeds in. Saving seeds is a way to collect them for the next year and it doesn't cost much. Most people throw away the seeds from the fresh vegetables and fruits they eat.

Instruct your members to keep some of the seeds the next time they eat fresh tomatoes, peppers, watermelons or other seed-bearing fruits and vegetables. Seeds should be removed from the vegetables and allowed to dry on paper towels. Later, gather like seeds together into small groups and place them into seed packets; tomato seeds will be in one packet and cucumber seeds will be in another. Do not overfill the seed envelopes. The packets should not bulge and seeds should fill one-half of the available space. The number of seeds in a group may vary with seed type and the size of envelope used. Place the sealed envelopes in an airtight container such as a plastic bag and store in a cool dry location (a refrigerator is perfect). Your gardeners will appreciate storing their seeds in a central location for easy access and organization of their seed bank.

Seeds that are encased in a fleshy pulp, like tomatoes, require a little more effort, but work very well. Squeeze the tomato pulp into a jar half-full of water. Then shake the jar vigorously to help separate pulp from seed. Place the mixture in a strainer and repeatedly spray with water to further remove the pulp. Allow the pulp-free seed to dry on a paper towel before storing.

A clean coffee can, plastic container or shoe box can work well as a seed bank. (A shoe box may insulate the seeds from cooler temperatures better than a thinner material and may keep the seed from spoiling as fast.) Have your group create and decorate its own seed bank. Ask members to cut out the Made by Nature seed packets/envelopes (Appendix B, page 119-120) and glue them together. Lay the label side (front) down on a flat surface such as a table and fold the two side flaps (longest flaps) together along the dotted line. The two flaps should overlap with the dotted lines on the inside of the envelope. Glue the two side flaps together. Be sure to use only enough glue to secure the sides together; excess glue may prevent the envelope from opening. Fold the short bottom flap up and glue it to the side flaps.

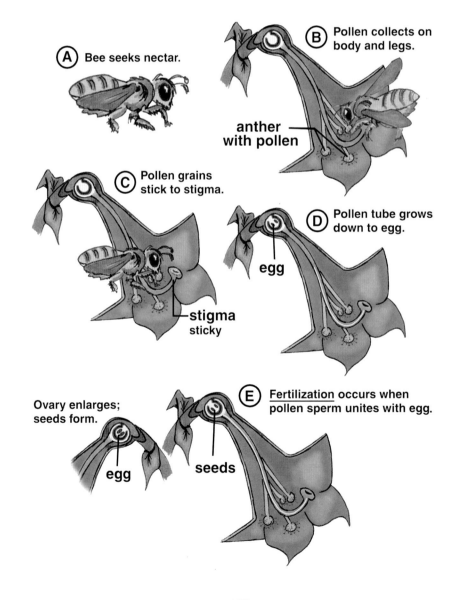

Your Made by Nature envelopes are ready to use after the glue has dried. Before filling with saved seed, write the type of seed, such as tomato or lettuce, and the day's date on the front of the envelope. House the collected seed in your decorated seed bank and store in a cool dry place until needed. Most seed will last up to 1 year in a refrigerator.

In no time your group will have a large assortment of seeds to trade and use in future gardens. It's fun to plant and watch Made by Nature seeds grow.

The plants that grow from Made by Nature seeds may look and taste slightly different than their parents. Flowers can be pollinated by a variety of similar plants, a process called "open pollination." Pollinating insects and wind are capable of carrying pollen from flower to flower. Fertilization occurs only when the pollen from one plant lands on a similar, compatible plant. If a pollen grain from a pumpkin flower is carried to and unites with a squash flower, fruit can then develop. The resulting fruit will have traits from both parents. Open pollination is one way nature provides new varieties of fruits and plants.

In the Classroom

Include a youth entrepreneurial component in this activity. Gardeners can choose to sell the saved seed in a fund-raising project, donate their seed or give the funds the group raises to their community as part of a community service project.

Have gardeners calculate how much money they saved using the saved seed. Local nurseries or gardening catalogs can help your gardeners determine current costs of seed. They also can calculate how much they earned and the profits made from the project. If used as a community service project, have gardeners calculate how much the group donated in terms of dollars and cents.

Swap Shop Eats

Objective: To understand and practice using a bartering system in exchanging surplus
foods for needed foods
Time: 45 minutes
Materials: Surplus of fruits and vegetables

Harvest time is a special time for gardeners. They are finally able to see the fruits of their labor.

Explain that during the Gold Rush days, a disease known as "scurvy" was a problem among people.
Scurvy was caused from a lack of vitamin C in the body. The miners during the Gold Rush so valued
potatoes for the vitamin C content that the miners actually traded gold for potatoes. Yes, gold! Ask the
gardeners how much gold a potato is worth today.

As a group, barter with one another for fruits and vegetables that are needed by a gardener. If a
gardener has grown all tomatoes in a plot and another gardener has grown all green beans, then the first
person has plenty of tomatoes but is lacking in green beans. Explain to the group that each participant
will trade for needed vegetables. Each gardener should end up with a variety of five different fruits and
vegetables for a total of 1 day's serving of fruits and vegetables.

Each gardener sets a price for the vegetables that will be traded. One potato might be worth 10 green
beans, or it might be worth two green beans. Ask the gardeners to trade or exchange with one another
simultaneously until everyone has finished bidding and obtained at least five needed items or has run
out of vegetables to trade. Let the gardeners work the crowd with as little help from the leader as
possible. Gardeners will have fun trading with one another while learning the value of food. Later, have
the group members discuss what was traded and the values different individuals placed on their food
items.

As an Extension
Following the group discussion, explain to the members that they should be eating between three to five
servings of vegetables each day and two to four servings of fruit a day. Use MyPyramid or other props
as visual aids. Encourage your gardeners to eat a variety of different fruits and vegetables as often as
possible.

In the Classroom
Gardeners can embellish their bartering day by enacting an
era in conjunction with the Swap Shop. They may consider
creating a medieval market, farmer's market during pioneer
days, or another period in time. Ask them to design and
decorate elaborate signs from cardboard or poster board to
help re-create the era. Ask gardeners to brainstorm on other
props to include.

Food Safety

Harvest time means it is time to enjoy eating the fruits and vegetables from your garden. Gardeners can appreciate the "fruits of their labor" for a long time by storing their surplus produce in a variety of ways.

The most important thing to do after harvest is to use proper storage and preservation practices to keep foods safe and of good quality. Ripe fruits and vegetables need special care and handling after being picked from the plant. This is the time when the most damage can occur. To ensure quality, maintain nutritional content and extend the shelf life of these food products, gardeners need to treat their harvest with extra care and attention.

Help your gardeners learn practical ways to keep their harvest safe and ways to preserve items for later use. Remember, not all families have a freezer or even a refrigerator to preserve food items. It is extremely important for everyone to have storage choices.

Gardeners will learn and practice safety measures in handling harvested fruits and vegetables to help keep their foods safe and nutritious.

ACTIVITIES

Safety First, Garden to the Table, Bold Molds
Party Confetti Salad, Save It

HELPFUL BACKGROUND INFORMATION

In the garden–Keep safety in mind and remember to keep garden environments safe for your young gardeners. When using manure in your compost pile, be sure it is completely composted. Some food-borne diseases can be transmitted through manure that is fresh or has not been thoroughly composted.

At harvest–To harvest fresh fruits and vegetables, use a clean, sharp knife or clippers to cut ripe produce from the plant. Be very careful when using sharp harvest equipment with young gardeners. Use cutting equipment you deem appropriate for your group. Collect produce in a clean harvest basket or container and discard diseased garden foods.

Wash hands with warm water and soap before handling any food. Encourage youths to wash the harvested fruits and vegetables, with water only, before eating.

Although gardening can be done in environmentally friendly ways, pesticides, herbicides, and insecticides can be carried distances through the air or through physical contact of fruits and vegetables with a shovel, hoe or hose. Thus, it's very important to wash the harvested produce to help keep foods safe.

Gardeners should understand that a few insect holes or some wind damage in produce does not make the entire piece of fruit or vegetable unusable. The damaged area can be cut out to leave a safe, edible piece of produce. Cut away the unwanted area(s) with a clean, sharp knife. Wash the knife with soap and warm water immediately before and after use.

Fresh fruits and vegetables from the garden should be properly refrigerated or stored within 2 hours after picking. Although the fruit or vegetable has been severed from the parent plant, respiration and enzymatic activities continue inside. Place harvested food items in the refrigerator to help slow these internal activities.

In the kitchen–The four most commonly transmitted bacteria that cause food-borne illnesses are E. coli, salmonella, shigella and campylobacter. These pathogens can be transmitted through cross-contamination from animal products. To help prevent contamination of fresh fruits and vegetables, be sure to wash hands thoroughly and clean all food preparation surfaces and utensils such as cutting boards, knives, forks, etc., with warm water and soap, especially after cutting meat, fish and poultry. Follow with a sanitizing agent such as a weak bleach solution (1 teaspoon of chlorine bleach to 1 quart of water). This is especially important to use on cutting boards.

Safety tip: After cutting meats, poultry, fish, or trimming freshly harvested produce, be sure to clean all utensils, cutting surfaces and hands with soap and warm water before continuing with food preparation. Taking these precautions will help prevent the spread of pathogens that can cause food-borne illness.

Most produce will last longer if it is kept in a refrigerator or preserved and stored for future use. Refrigeration helps slow down internal ripening activity within the fruit or vegetable. However, some fruits and vegetables, such as bananas, whole onions, and tomatoes, can be damaged by refrigeration. Allow unripe tomatoes to ripen before refrigeration because tomatoes will not ripen further in cool environments.

Cooking can diminish the nutrient value of fruits and vegetables:

Most nutrient content

Fresh

Baked/Steamed

Blanched

Boiled

Least nutrient content

Preservation: Blanching vegetables before freezing helps foods keep their quality, freshness, color and texture. Blanch vegetables by submerging in a pot of boiling water for 1 to 4 minutes, drain, then immediately submerge in a pot of ice water or hold under cool running water. Cool for as long as the blanching time. This cooling is needed to stop the vegetables from cooking further. Remove the vegetables from the water and drain thoroughly. Place in airtight containers and label with the name and date (i.e., broccoli, Jan. 1, 2000). Store in the freezer.

For each pound of vegetables, use a minimum of 1 gallon of boiling water in the pot to blanch. Begin timing when the vegetable is first put into the boiling water. Cover the pot during the blanching process to help keep the water boiling at all times. Use the following table as a guide to blanching some common garden vegetables.

COMMON GARDEN VEGETABLES

Beans, Lima, small	2 minutes
Beans, Lima, medium	3 minutes
Broccoli	3 minutes
Cabbage	1½ minutes
Carrots, diced	2 minutes
Green peppers, slices	2 minutes
Greens (kale, mustard, turnip greens)	2 minutes
Peas, medium	1½ minutes
Spinach	1½ minutes
Squash (summer)	3 minutes
Sweet corn (on cob)	4 minutes
Tomatoes (raw)	30-60 seconds to loosen skins

Stewed tomatoes: Remove the stem end, peel and quarter the tomatoes. Cover and cook until tender (about 10 to 20 minutes). Immediately place the pan containing the tomatoes into ice water to cool.

For additional information or information on freezing fruits contact your local county Extension office or visit the Food and Consumer Sciences Web site at http://fcs.tamu.edu.

RECOMMENDED STORAGE MATERIALS

Freezers: Freezers should be checked periodically for temperature accuracy. The recommended freezer temperature to keep fruits and vegetables at best quality is 0 degrees F. Even 10 degrees F warmer can cause foods to break down and spoil faster.

Resealable Plastic Bags: Use freezer-grade resealable airtight plastic bags. Be sure to remove as much oxygen as possible from the bag before freezing. Respiration occurs at a slower rate and food deterioration slows in containers with less oxygen. Each bag should contain only the amount to be served at one time. If storing more than one serving in one large-sized freezer bag, remove the bag from the freezer just prior to use and return it immediately after using.

Other activities that could be used to support this teaching concept include Beauty Contest, page 81, and Garden to the Table, page 53.

Safety First

Objective: To understand and practice food safety rules
Time: 30 minutes
Materials: Cutting board, sheets of stickers

BEFORE THIS ACTIVITY

Germs are everywhere in the environment. One coin can potentially contain more than a million different germs. Not all of these are harmful, but it is important to realize possible hazards. Children constantly are touching objects to better understand their environment and world in which they live. Without realizing it, they pick up germs with each object they touch. Thus, it's important that they learn the necessity of washing hands and fresh produce before eating. Refer to the background information for additional food safety tips.

LET THE FUN BEGIN!

ASK PARTICIPANTS THE FOLLOWING QUESTIONS:

1. What should you do before crossing the street?
2. What should you do if a stranger asks you to go with them to look for a lost puppy?
3. What should you do if you see a small child playing with matches?

Have one of the gardeners tell what the word safety means. Ask the gardeners why they want to be safe. Explain that if they are being safe, they are protecting themselves from danger. Next, ask them if they think they have to be safe with their food.

Explain that being safe with food means doing things to make sure their food is properly handled, stored, preserved and served. Share with them the saying,

Just clean the surface.

Make sure to wash your hands.

Garden veggies should be rinsed—
gets rid of soil, bugs and sand.

Explain that germs like bacteria and molds on foods can make them sick if not removed before eating. Tell the learners that germs are everywhere and the best way to be safe is to make sure that anything that goes in their mouths is very clean. Ask them to make a list of all the things they have touched that day: desk, books, door knobs, dishes, countertops, kitchen towels, sinks, playground ball, etc. Ask them if they would want to touch their mouths to any of those items. Explain that if we eat food with our hands, bacteria that might be on any those items can end up in our mouths. Emphasize the importance of washing hands and its important role in preventing illness.

Ask them why it is important to wash the vegetables they grow or get from the store. Have they ever had to throw away a piece of candy because it fell on the ground? The harvested vegetables have been on or near the ground for quite some time. Washing and sometimes scrubbing helps to remove all sorts of things like soil, insects, tiny organisms that are too small to be seen, and chemicals like pesticides and fertilizer.

Hold up a cutting board and ask them what it is. Explain that a cutting board is one of the best hiding places for germs. Sometimes people make a mistake and use the same board to cut up both raw meat and fresh vegetables. Explain that it is a good idea to use one cutting board for meats and a different one for vegetables. Have the gardeners learn the safety saying above and perform it to each other.
Then pass out the sheets of stickers. When your learners go home, their job is to place the stickers on places that germs could be hiding and that need to be cleaned regularly. Have them make a list of the items or places where they put the stickers and bring that list to the next meeting to share.

As an Extension

Introduce more food safety information. Videotape a cooking show and have learners identify the potential hazards. Have them look for things such as using fingers to taste or test the temperature of the food, or cross-contamination by using the same dish towel to wipe hands after cutting raw meat and vegetables, or failing to wash hands after touching the nose or mouth. Have the group discuss each potential problem and the safest way to handle each situation.

Garden to the Table

Objective: To determine harvest time of various garden vegetables
Time: Variable
Materials: Ready-to-harvest vegetables in the garden

Before the Lesson

Some fruits and vegetables can be stored at room temperature without spoiling, if they are eaten the same day as harvested. Produce will last longer if stored in a refrigerator or preserved for future use. Refrigeration helps slow internal activity within the fruit or vegetable. Potatoes, onions and pumpkins are exceptions and should be stored in a cool, dry, dark place such as a cabinet or bin.

To harvest fruits and vegetables, use a clean harvest knife or clippers to cut the ripe produce from a plant. Be very careful when using sharp harvest equipment with young gardeners. Use cutting equipment you deem appropriate for your group. Collect produce in a harvest basket or container. Cut out areas from fruits and vegetables that are spoiled, insect damaged or over ripened.

It is important that youths understand that just because a fruit or vegetable contains a few insect holes or some wind damage, this does not make the entire fruit or vegetable unusable. The damaged areas may be cut out to leave a safe, edible piece of produce to be used immediately or preserved. Cut out the unusable portion(s) with a clean knife. Remember to clean the knife immediately with soap and warm water before using it again. These practices will help keep foods safe.

LET THE FUN BEGIN!

One of the most exciting times for any gardener is time to harvest. As harvest time nears, ask your students how they know when it is time to pick the produce. The length of time from planting to harvest will vary, depending on what crops are growing. The guide below will help your group know when to harvest.

Have you ever thumped a watermelon, squeezed a tomato or shaken a cantaloupe? Produce for sale at a market or grocery store may not be very good because it is not fresh or is not yet ripe. You already know not to buy vegetables that have bad spots on them. Also, don't choose anything that is soft or mushy. Try these tricks next time you go shopping so you can select the best produce.

Stick your thumbnail into a corn cob kernel. Choose corn that is juicy.

Hold a tomato and gently squeeze it. Buy tomatoes that are a little firm but not hard.

Choose peppers that are firm when you squeeze them.

Look for green lettuce that is not slimy or wilted.

Break a green bean in half. Use them only if they are crisp and snap in two.

When you eat broccoli, you are eating flower buds that haven't opened. If you see any yellow flowers, the broccoli is old. Also, the broccoli should be crisp.

Shake a cantaloupe. You should buy the fruit if you hear the seeds inside rattle and it has a strong cantaloupe smell.

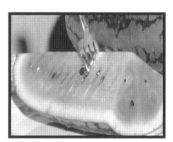

A good watermelon makes a "thud" sound when you thump it.

Make sure to discuss proper washing and preparation methods for vegetables. To keep fresh vegetables longer, wash them just prior to using. Prepare greens by rinsing the leaves in cool running water to remove soil particles and any small organisms that might be living deep in the center of the leaves. Hard-coated or thick-skinned fruit and root crops should be rinsed and scrubbed lightly with a vegetable brush, if needed.

Now it's time to harvest. Have gardeners work together or divide them into small groups. Use reference on previous page to explain to gardeners the harvest stage for each vegetable in their garden. In the garden area, look at each vegetable one by one. Have gardeners repeat out loud what the correct harvest stage is for each vegetable. Groups work together and harvest only vegetables that meet the criteria. Afterwards, allow gardeners to handle and examine the vegetables.

In the Classroom

Create a song or poem to help gardeners remember the harvest stage for each vegetable. For example a verse might include:

Watermelons can be picked when they're green and round only when you thump them they make a dull, hollow sound.

Have gardeners write the words to the song or use a computer. Print each gardener a copy.

Bold Molds

Objective: To experiment with foods to understand the benefits of proper storage of after harvesting from the garden
Time: 30 minutes
Materials: Ripe fruits, toothpicks, rubbing alcohol, resealable or self-sealing plastic bags, refrigerator, shady and sunny locations, Bold Molds Lab Sheet (Appendix B, page 135)

BEFORE THE LESSON:

Spoilage from bacteria or fungi can occur before or after harvest, depending on the type of fruit or vegetable, the invading organism, and the storage method used. Depending on the type of organism, molds that attack plants can appear as different colors on the outer layer of the skin. Some microorganisms have the ability to secrete toxins that can spread and infect other parts of the fruit or vegetable, which lessens its nutrient value, makes it unsafe to eat, and wastes gardeners' time, energy and space.

Any plant part can become infected with a postharvest disease. The bacteria or fungi are usually present in the garden and can easily attack the fruit or vegetable through the skin. Usually the harder or thicker the skin or peel, the less likely it is that infection will occur. This means tomatoes, strawberries and such are more easily infected by bacteria or fungi. Apple, kiwi and cucumber are less susceptible than thin-skinned plant parts. Oranges, lemons, limes and various nuts are the most difficult for pathogens to enter.

Don't confuse molds with insect damage or damage caused by wind or hail. Insect damage can appear as small holes and may affect only a minute piece of the fruit. Wind or hail damage can appear as small indentations or abrasions and the skin can be intact or ruptured.

It is important that youths understand that a few insect holes or some wind damage to a fruit or vegetable does not make the entire piece unusable. Damaged areas can be cut out to leave a safe, edible piece of produce to be used immediately or preserved for later. Cut out the unusable portion(s) with a clean sharp knife. Remember to clean the knife immediately with soap and warm water before using it again.

Let the Fun Begin!

Explain to gardeners that it is important to properly store fruits and vegetables within 2 hours after picking from the plant. Even though picked from the plant, activity continues in fruits and vegetables. This activity, called respiration, is similar to breathing and other activities that occur in people when they are asleep. As foods get older, spoilage bacteria and fungi, called molds, can grow and cause foods to spoil. Storing foods properly helps slow down spoilage.

Have the gardeners conduct a fair or impartial science experiment testing fruits or vegetables in three different locations. Explain that this experiment will test how the temperatures of different locations affect mold growth on fresh fruits and vegetables. Explain that a scientific experiment must have constants and only one variable. A variable is something that can change or is different. In this experiment, the food items are called a constant because they are identical (three strawberries, three kiwi or three apples). The variable is the three storage locations. Have gardeners choose three locations based on temperature: (1) a shaded area, such as a dry cabinet (2) direct sunlight, i.e. a sunny window, and (3) a very cold refrigerator.

Ask gardeners to thoroughly wash their hands before beginning the experiment to prevent the possibility of introducing outside germs. **1.** Pass out resealable or self-sealing plastic bags, rubbing alcohol and toothpicks. **2.** Have gardeners dip the toothpicks in the alcohol and punch through both sides of the plastic bags only once. **3.** Place each fruit or vegetable in its own bag and put three bags (constants) in the three locations (variable).

To exclude light as a possible contributor in the experiment, place fruit in a shoebox or like container before placing the box in the sunny location. Punch small holes in the box along one side to allow air to circulate. This box is needed only for the sunny location since cabinets and refrigerators usually stay dark. If using strawberries as a constant, place one bag of strawberries in the refrigerator, one in a dry dark cabinet and one in a box placed in a warm, sunny location.

Have gardeners complete the first part of the Bold Molds Lab Sheet (page 135). The results portion will be completed 1 or 2 weeks later. Consider choosing small groups to conduct concurrent experiments: one group testing soft-coated (thin-skinned) items, a second testing medium-coated fruits or vegetables, etc. Discuss the results with gardeners as to which location(s) best preserved each food used.

Fruit and Veggie Samples

- Thin-skinned samples: ripe strawberries, bananas, peppers, green onions or tomatoes
- Medium-skinned samples: ripe mango, apples, kiwi, cucumber, radishes or potatoes
- Thick-skinned samples: oranges, lemons, limes or various nuts

As an Extension

Test the effects of washing fruits or vegetables before storing versus washing them just prior to eating. Or, test the effects of not washing hands, reusing a resealable plastic bag, coughing on produce or rolling fruits and vegetables across countertops. Your group can use the Bold Molds Lab Sheet (page 135) to record these results, too.

Party Confetti Salad

Objective: To demonstrate the preparation of a salad using vegetables harvested from the garden
Time: 25 minutes
Materials: Various vegetables, salad dressing, crackers, pencils, paper

Plan a day to harvest various vegetables from the garden and make a salad, or ask gardeners to bring a couple of their favorite vegetables to add to a group salad. Allow each learner to show which vegetable was picked or brought and explain why it was chosen. As a different vegetable is introduced, talk about how it is usually prepared or cut in making a salad. For example, after washing a bell pepper, its insides are removed and then it is cut into chunks, slices or rings.

Spend some time discussing the importance of rinsing fruits and vegetables to get rid of insects, soil, chemicals and other tiny organisms. Potatoes and many crops that grow below ground level should be scrubbed in order to remove the soil that clings to the skin. Allow learners to clean their vegetables before preparing.

If a vegetable can be prepared with a butter knife, allow the student to do so. Once all produce is prepared, have the group pick up a bowl and add all of the ingredients of their choice to their salad. Make sure to have crackers and different salad dressings to complement the salad.

In the Classroom

Make a class graph or list of the vegetables students picked or brought, showing the total number for each item. Depending on the grade level, students could create simple picture graphs or bar graphs or a more complicated pie graph.

Have each student make a list of questions to ask of their peers when reading the graph. Compile the questions and write them up for the class to answer based on the information collected in the graph.

Save It

Objective: To practice frozen storage method for fruits and vegetables
Time: 45 minutes
Materials: Freezer, freezer bags, waterproof pen, cookie sheet

Before the Lesson

Follow proper freezing instructions when freezing fruits or vegetables. Most vegetables will need to be blanched before freezing to help preserve the quality and freshness (includes color and texture). See the background information on page 50-51.

To freeze, line a tray or cookie sheet with wax paper or plastic. Place small whole fruits or vegetables, such as beans, peas, strawberries and pieces of larger fruits and vegetables in a single layer on the lined tray. Cut large items into smaller-sized pieces if needed. Foods such as broccoli stems can be left whole or cut into bite-size pieces for quicker freezing. Space between pieces allows quicker freeze time and use of individual pieces. Pieces that are allowed to touch can freeze together, which makes it difficult to use.

After freezing, the individual pieces should be quickly bagged into a freezer-grade resealable airtight plastic bag or container. Exclude as much oxygen from the bag as possible. Use a size bag that works well for its intended usage. A single bag works well for single servings. Quart or gallon size bags work well for families to store larger quantities for use in several meals.

If using larger bags for multiple meals, remove the container from the freezer just prior to use, then immediately return it to the freezer to help keep the foods safe and frozen. If allowed to thaw, pieces may stick together when refrozen, making it difficult to use the next time.

Successful Steps in Freezing Foods

Good Quality Food: The quality of the food coming out of the freezer is only as good as the quality of the food before it was frozen.

Careful Preparation: This helps to control growth of bacteria and molds and stops internal enzymatic activity. Read and follow food preservation instructions carefully.

Proper Packaging: Use moisture and vapor-proof packaging materials to prevent evaporation and to retain nutrient value, color, flavor and texture. Suitable containers include wide-mouth can-or-freeze glass jars, freezer quality plastic containers, freezer bags placed inside freezer cardboard containers, and freezer-grade self-lock plastic bags. Be sure to eliminate as much air as possible to preserve food quality.

Loading the Freezer: Freeze foods at 0 degrees °F immediately after packaging. Keep remaining packages in a refrigerator until they can be transferred to the freezer. Overloading the freezer slows down the freezing rate. Be sure to leave space between packages to allow air to circulate freely. Arrange the freezer so the food frozen the longest will be used first.

Length of Storage: Length of time that frozen foods will maintain quality in frozen storage depends on:

* proper handling before freezing
* packaging material used
* storage temperature and
* kind of food stored.

Additional information can be obtained from the Food and Consumer Sciences Web site http://fcs.tamu.edu or from your local county Extension office.

LET THE FUN BEGIN!

Ask the group how their families preserve food items and why they preserve food. Explain that foods stored correctly in a refrigerator can be safe to eat 1 week to a month later. Storage time can differ, depending on the food item and storage method used.

Ask them if their grandmothers have ever canned fresh fruits or vegetables. Explain that this is a good way to save foods for later use and that people have used canning for many years. Canning is a process that takes time and space and it is very important to do the canning process correctly in order to keep the food safe. You might also consider inviting a guest to demonstrate a canning process and involve the gardeners to give them first-hand experience. Allow an additional 45 minutes when including a demonstration.

Explain that today they are going to learn and practice a quick and safer method of saving fresh fruits and vegetables called "tray freezing," which they can do at home.

Gardeners can pick ripe fruits and vegetables from the garden or they can visit a pick-your-own orchard, or purchase fruits and vegetables from a farmer's market or local supermarket.

Remind gardeners to practice safety rules in the garden and wash their hands before and after picking fresh fruits and vegetables. Explain that these are fresh foods and because they are fresh they bruise and damage easily. Ask them to handle their harvest with care, much like they would handle an egg. Bruised skins of fruits and vegetables spoil faster and develop diseases easier than nonbruised skins.

After washing the fruits and vegetables, help gardeners cut them into bite-size pieces, if necessary. Vegetables should be blanched or precooked in boiling water before freezing as needed. Length of precooking or blanching depends upon the type of vegetables and size of the pieces. (See basic blanching information for common vegetables on page 50-51.) Place the pieces in a single layer on a clean, dry cookie sheet lined with wax paper or plastic.

Caution gardeners that the pieces will freeze together if they are touching each other. Place the cooking sheet in the freezer until all the individual pieces are frozen. The time to freeze will vary depending on the type and thickness of the fruit or vegetable. Once frozen, have gardeners quickly collect them into resealable freezer-grade bags, and return them to the freezer. Do NOT let the pieces thaw.

For comparison purposes, have gardeners wash whole fruits or vegetables, such as huge strawberries or broccoli heads, and place them into similar containers and freeze. Remember to pre-cook or blanch the food as needed.

After the bags with individual pieces are frozen, have gardeners examine the bags. Large pieces such as whole broccoli will take longer to freeze than smaller individual pieces. Ask the gardeners why is it a good idea to freeze individual pieces. (You may choose to freeze an entire broccoli head or freeze the florets individually. Be sure to explain to your group that broccoli is a vegetable that freezes well and can be frozen in larger pieces.)

ABC's of Healthful Eating

You might consider fresh fruits and vegetables as the original fast foods: pick 'em, wash 'em, eat 'em and go! To get the 1½ cups of fruit and 1½ cups of vegetables that kids your age need each day, try to include them in your meals and snacks. The more colorful the fruits and vegetables that you put on your plate, the better!

Research shows that children are more willing to try eating fruits and vegetables when they actually grow them themselves. Using these gardening activities, your group will have the opportunity to taste unfamiliar fruits and vegetables, and learn where they come from, their vitamin and mineral contents, and their importance in a well-balanced diet.

> Young gardeners will learn that different fruits and vegetables provide some essential vitamins and minerals the body needs to stay strong and healthy.

ACTIVITIES

MyPyramid, Label Reader, Taste Test, Rough and Tough Foods, U-B the Judge, Fruit and Veggie Mania, Beauty Contest, Healing Powers

Gardeners can grow beautiful, nutritious fruits and vegetables in their home gardens. All it takes is a little work and TLC (tender loving care) to experience home-grown fruits and vegetables, depending on your location. Many local grocery and specialty markets have a variety of fresh fruits and vegetables. International markets make numerous varieties of apples, bananas, and some citrus available 365 days of the year.

Fruits and vegetables contain many necessary vitamins and minerals for healthy growth and living. The following activities focus on nutrients vitamin A, vitamin C, calcium, iron and fiber.

Gardening: In Step with the Dietary Guidelines for Americans

The Dietary Guidelines are nutrition and health recommendations for healthy children (ages 2 years and older) and adults of any age. Every 5 years, the Dietary Guidelines are evaluated and revised to ensure they are current with the latest research on nutrition and health.

Aim for Fitness

Aim for healthy weight—How much you eat and how active you are affects how much you weigh.

Be physically active each day—Gardening can be a productive and fun way to get the physical activity needed for health.

Build a Healthy Base

Let MyPyramid guide your food choices. To get the nutrients you need to be healthy, eat moderate amounts of different kinds of foods.

Choose a variety of grains daily, especially whole grains—bread, tortillas, corn bread, rice and pasta taste great and give you the energy you need to make it through the day.

Choose a variety of fruits and vegetables daily—fruits and vegetables add color and taste and bring a smile to everyone's face.

Keep foods safe to eat—wash your hands, fruits and vegetables before eating, and heat and store foods properly.

Choose Sensibly

Choose a diet that is low in saturated fat and cholesterol and moderate in total fat—Plant foods such as fruits, vegetables and grains do not contain cholesterol and most are low in fat.

Choose beverages and foods to moderate your intake of sugars. Fruit and 100 percent fruit juice are naturally sweet.

Choose and prepare foods with less salt—Use herbs, onions and garlic to add flavor.

MyPyramid

The origin of any food, from hamburger to oil, can be traced back to the foods in the first three sections on the left side of MyPyramid, and they are all derived from plants. They are the grains, vegetables, and fruits groups. Although the meat group also includes some plant-derived foods, most items are animal sources.

MyPyramid is the most recent development in nutrition education. It divides food into groups and makes specific recommendations of amounts that a person needs from each group. The food groups that should be eaten the most are in the largest slices of the pyramid. Foods that should be eaten sparingly are in the narrow slices of the pyramid. MyPyramid also stresses the importance of physical activity in a healthy lifestyle.

By using MyPyramid online, you can customize your diet for your age, sex, and physical activity level. Each person has individual dietary needs. To customize your diet, visit www.mypyramid.gov.

Recommended Amounts from Each Food Group

Most of us do not know how much of different foods we need to eat. Below are examples of healthy food choices and the amounts that a youth age 8 or older needs each day.*

Food Group	Examples of healthy food choices	Amount needed/day
Grains	1 slice whole-grain bread (1 ounce) ½ cup rice, pasta, or cooked cereal (1 ounce) 4 wheat crackers (1 ounce)	6 ounces
Fruit	1 medium-sized fruit (1 cup) ½ grapefruit or small melon (½ cup) ½ cup of berries ½ cup of diced, cooked, or canned fruit ¾ cup of 100% juice ¼ cup of dried fruit	2½ cups
Vegetable	½ cup of vegetables—cooked or raw 1 cup of leafy vegetables—raw ½ cup of dry beans or dry peas ¾ cup 100% juice	1½ cups
Milk	1 cup of low-fat milk 1 slice of low-fat cheese (counts as 1 cup) 1 container (6-ounce) of low-fat yogurt (¾ cup)	3 cups
Meats & Beans	1 cup of dry beans or dry peas (2 ounces) 1 tablespoon of peanut butter (1 ounce) 1 fillet baked fish (3½ ounces) 1 grilled pork chop (3 ounces) 1 medium slice of lean roast (1½ ounces)	5 ounces

*Based on a 1,800-calorie diet.
For more information on the amounts that are right for you, see www.mypyramid.gov.

Needed Nutrients for Health and Nutrition

The human body needs proteins, fats, carbohydrates, water, minerals and vitamins. No single food contains all of the necessary nutrients required for good health and nutrition. It is important to eat a variety of foods to maximize vitamin and mineral intake.

Proteins: A healthy body needs 22 protein building blocks called "amino acids." Some of these building blocks are naturally produced in the body while the remaining 13 building blocks need to be eaten in the diet.

Function: Builds body and repairs tissue; provides energy; regulates body functions; helps transport nutrients and oxygen.

Plant Sources: Nuts, dry beans, dry peas, peanut butter.

Fats: Contrary to popular belief, fats are needed for good body function. Total daily fat intake should be 30 percent or less of the total energy intake. Regulating fat intake may help decrease the risk of heart disease and obesity.

> **Function:** *Helps absorb and transport specific vitamins (fat soluble vitamins A, D, E and K), cushions vital body organs, supplies essential fatty acids, insulates the body, protects nerves and blood vessels, serves as a source of stored energy.*

> **Plant Sources:** *Olives, avocado, coconut, nuts, olive oil, vegetable oil.*

Carbohydrates: Should be consumed most frequently since body uses carbohydrates for energy. Sugar, starch and fiber are three types of carbohydrates.

> ✐ **Sugar:** *Simplest form found in body; easiest to use by body.*

> ✐ **Starch:** *Found in roots, legumes, grains and vegetables; changes into simple sugars through digestion and is used by the body.*

> ✐ **Fiber:** *Found only in plant parts; includes whole grain cereals, fruits, vegetables; is NOT digestible by humans.*

> **Function:** *Main source of energy; fiber aids in digestion*

> **Plant Sources:** *Includes bread, cereals, rice, corn, fruit and vegetables.*

Water: Sometimes referred to as the "forgotten nutrient;" important for all living organisms. The human body contains more than 70 percent water; plants contain 80 to 95 percent water.

> **Function:** *Aids in digestion; lubricates bones and joints; regulates internal (body) temperatures.*

> **Plant Sources:** *Fruit and vegetable beverages; all fresh fruits and vegetables.*

Minerals: The information below focuses on the essential vitamins and minerals as listed on most food labels. Additional nutritional information can be obtained from the USDA Web site or from your local county Extension office.

Some Nutrients Needed for Proper Human Bodily Function

Mineral	Function	Plant Sources
Calcium	Promotes strong bones and teeth; needed for blood to coagulate or thicken; used by muscles and nerves.	Leafy dark green vegetables, broccoli
Iron	Needed for hemoglobin (the part or the red blood cells that carries oxygen) and myoglobin (the protein in muscle cells that holds oxygen).	Dried legumes, leafy green vegetables, dried fruit, hole grains breads, enriched breads
Zinc	Helps lungs release oxygen; strengthens the immune system.	Wheat bran

Vitamin	Function	Plant Sources
Vitamin C (ascorbic acid)	Helps fight infections and heals wounds; helps the body absorb iron.	Oranges, citrus fruits, cantaloupe, strawberries, dark leafy green vegetables, broccoli, cabbage, green peppers
Vitamin A (retinol)	Helps with night vision; helps bones grow and skin develop; helps fight disease.	Carrots, sweet potatoes, spinach, broccoli, apricots, cantaloupe, peaches, watermelon

Other activities that could be used to support teaching concepts are Fruit and Veggie Lab, page 87; Bean Tepee, page 36; Apple Surprise, page 88; Party Confetti Salad, page 57; Save It, page 58; Strip Chips, page 94; Garden to the Table, page 53; Robust Rainbow Recipes, page 92; Bold Molds, page 55; Plan 10 in 2, page 43; Sack of Potatoes, page 33; and Symmetry Snack II, page 90.

Fruits and Vegetables: Nutritious and Delicious

Fruits and vegetables are both tasty and nutritious. Fruits and most vegetables are fat- and sodium-free and can help us meet our daily need for several nutrients, including vitamin A, vitamin C, calcium, iron and fiber.

Vitamin A: This nutrient helps us see in the dark, promotes the growth and repair of tissues, prevents the drying of skin and eyes, and helps our body fight infections. The form of vitamin A found in plants, beta-carotene, acts as an antioxidant.

Good Sources of Vitamin A (contains at least 10 percent daily value)			
Apricots	Brussels sprouts	Guava	Tangerine
Avocado	Cherries	Papaya	Tomato/tomato juice
Black-eyed peas	Green peas	Romaine lettuce	Watermelon
Excellent Sources of Vitamin A (contains at least 20 percent daily value)			
Broccoli	Collard greens	Persimmon	Turnip greens
Cantaloupe	Mango	Pumpkin	Winter squash
Carrots	Mustard greens	Spinach	
Chinese cabbage	Nectarine	Sweet potato	

Vitamin C: This nutrient, also called ascorbic acid, helps our bodies fight infections and heal wounds. Vitamin C helps our bodies absorb the mineral iron and may also protect our body from some diseases by acting as an antioxidant.

Good Sources of Vitamin C (contains at least 10 percent daily value)			
Asparagus	Green beans	Nectarine	Plum
Avocado	Green peas	Okra	Pumpkin
Banana	Lentils	Peach	Spinach
Carrots	Navy beans	Pear	Winter squash
Excellent Sources of Vitamin C (contains at least 20 percent daily value)			
Blueberries	Grapefruit	Orange	Sweet potato
Broccoli	Guava	Orange juice	Swiss chard
Brussels sprouts	Honeydew melon	Papaya	Tangerine
Cauliflower	Kiwi	Pineapple	Tomato
Chinese cabbage	Mango	Strawberries	Turnip greens
Collard greens	Mustard greens	Sweet peppers	Watermelon

Calcium: This mineral promotes strong bones and teeth. Calcium is needed for our muscles (including the heart) to contract, and helps our blood clot when we get a cut or wound. Nerve cells use calcium to carry impulses to neighboring cells.

Good Sources of Calcium (contains at least 10 percent daily value)			
Collard greens	Spinach		Turnip greens

Iron: Our body uses iron to form hemoglobin and myoglobin, proteins that carry oxygen throughout our body.

Good Sources of Iron (contains at least 10 percent daily value)		
Black beans Lentils	Garbanzo beans (chickpeas) Spinach	Legumes (Lima, navy, pinto, kidney, and white beans)

Fiber: This nondigestible carbohydrate comes from plants in soluble or insoluble forms. Soluble fiber can lower blood cholesterol levels and may help the body regulate its blood sugar. Insoluble fiber, also called "roughage" helps prevent constipation by moving waste material through the digestive system. To learn more about fiber, see Rough and Tough Foods on page 75.

MyPyramid

Objective: To use MyPyramid to plan balanced meals
Time: 1 hour, 15 minutes
Materials: MyPyramid for Kids Poster (Appendix B, page 136; also available online at *http://www.mypyramid.gov/kids*); Making the Menu (Appendix B, page 137); (You may wish to send home copies of the supplemental parent sheets in Appendix C, the advanced MyPyramid for Kids Poster, page 154, and Pyramid Eating, pages 155–6, which is also available online at http://www.mypyramid.gov/professionals.)

Before the Lesson

The origin of any food—from hamburger to oil—can be traced back to the foods in the first three sections on the left side of MyPyramid, and these foods are all derived from plants. They are the grains, vegetables, and fruits groups. Although the meat group also includes some plant-derived foods, most of the foods are from animal sources.

MyPyramid is the most recent development in nutrition education. It divides food into groups and makes specific recommendations of amounts that a person needs from each group. The food groups that should be eaten the most are in the largest slices of the pyramid. Foods that should be eaten sparingly are in the narrow slices of the pyramid. MyPyramid also stresses the importance of physical activity in a healthy lifestyle.

By using MyPyramid online, you can customize your diet for your age, your sex, and your physical activity level. Each person has individual dietary needs. To customize your diet, visit www.mypyramid.gov. For educational purposes, some MyPyramid posters show the daily recommended servings for an individual requiring a 1,800 calorie/day diet.

Grains Group: This group is represented by the wide orange slice at the left side of MyPyramid. Try to include whole-grain products in at least half of your grain group selections. A 1,800-calorie/day diet needs 6 ounces of grain foods each day.

Vegetable Group: The Vegetable Group is represented by the green slice on MyPyramid. Vary your vegetables to gain the benefits of different phyto-chemicals. Most kids need 2½ cups of vegetables each day.

Fruit Group: The Fruit Group is represented by the red slice of MyPyramid. Fruits are nature's treat—they are sweet and delicious. Go easy on juices, and make sure they are 100 percent fruit juice. Most kids need 1½ cups of fruit each day.

Milk Group: The Milk Group is represented by the blue slice of MyPyramid. Milk products provide

the calcium needed for strong bones. Check the container to make sure your milk, cheese, or other dairy product is low fat or fat free. Kids ages 2 to 8 need 2 cups per day. Kids 9 and older need 3 cups of the milk group each day.

Meat & Beans Group: This group provides protein. Select lean or low-fat cuts of meat that have been baked, broiled, or grilled—not fried. Nuts, seeds, peas, and beans are great sources of protein that can be used in "meatless meals." Most kids need 5 ounces from the Meat & Bean Group daily.

MyPyramid For Kids

| Grains | Vegetables | Fruits | Oils | Milk | Meat & Beans |

Oils: The narrow yellow section of MyPyramid represents oils. Although oils are not a food group, some are needed for good health. Use oils in moderation. Get your oils from fish, nuts, and liquid oils such as corn oil, soybean oil, and canola oil.

Fats and sugars should be used in moderation. Limit solid fats as well as foods that contain them. Choose foods and beverages that are low in added sugars. Balance food and physical activity. Aim for at least 60 minutes of physical activity each day.

Because over half of MyPyramid include foods derived directly from plant sources, it is easy to see that plants play a key role in the human diet.

Remember, it is important to have a healthful, well-balanced diet. No single food contains all the necessary nutrients. It is important to eat a variety of foods and balance the diet with the recommended number of servings from each food group.

LET THE FUN BEGIN!

Ask the junior gardeners if they know that hamburgers come from plants. Have them imagine what a hamburger plant might look like. Ask volunteers to describe it to you and assign them to draw what they think a hamburger plant looks like.

Explain that hamburgers really do come from plants, but there is no such thing as a hamburger plant. Ask them to call out the ingredients found in hamburgers and write the ingredients on a chalkboard or poster. Tell them you will underline any word that names a plant. Go through each ingredient on the list that is not a plant and ask them where it comes from. Next to the ingredient, write where the ingredient originates. Keep writing until you find a link to plants.

Example:

buns ⟶ flour ⟶ _wheat_

meat ⟶ cows ⟶ feed on _grass, hay, grain_

cheese ⟶ dairy products ⟶ cows ⟶ feed on _grass, hay, grain_

lettuce

tomato

pickles

onion

mayonnaise → eggs ⟶ _chickens_ ⟶ feed on _grain_
→ vegetable oil ⟶ _peanut, olive, corn, canola_

mustard ⟶ _mustard seed_

catsup ⟶ _tomato_

Ask the learners if they have ever seen a pyramid. Tell them that the most famous pyramids in the world are in Egypt and that they are believed to be more than 4,000 years old. The pyramids were built without the help of power tools. All the labor was done by hand.

Ask the learners if they have heard of MyPyramid. Distribute copies of MyPyramid for Kids Worksheet (http://www.mypyramid.gov/kids). Tell them that the pyramids in Mexico and Central America were built by the Mayans and Aztecs. The pyramids were built with stairs so people could climb to the top.

MyPyramid also has stairs. The stairs on MyPyramid represent physical activity. The poster shows many kinds of physical activity. Part of being healthy is to be physically active. Gardening is one way to be physically active. Ask the learners to describe some of the ways they stay active.

Ask if they have noticed that some of the slices of the pyramid are wider than others. The different sizes remind us to choose more foods from the food groups that have the widest slices. Together the Grains Group (orange slice), Vegetables Group (green slice), and Fruits Group (red slice) represent over one half of the volume of MyPyramid. The Milk Group is represented by the blue slice, the Meats & Beans group is represented by the purple slice, and the narrow yellow slice is the Oils Group. Have the learners color in the sections of their MyPyramid and label the sections.

Ask the gardeners to determine the food group for each of the hamburger items listed on the board and then recite the amount needed from each food group each day.

Example:

buns —————————→ Cereal and Grain Group —————————→ 6 ounces

milk —————————→ Dairy Group —————————→ 3 cups
(2 cups for kids ages 2–8)

lettuce —————————→ Vegetable Group —————————→ 2–3 servings

hamburger —————————→ Meat & Beans Group —————————→ 2–3 servings

Next, use the following questions to lead a discussion of how to "read" MyPyramid:

- What is the largest section of the pyramid?
- What is the smallest section of MyPyramid?
- Why are certain foods are in big sections and some are in smaller sections? (The bigger sections show foods that we should eat more of, and the smaller sections show foods we should eat less of.)
- Have the learners call out examples of foods from each group.
- Who should follow MyPyramid carefully? (Everyone)
- Fruits and vegetables have their own sections on MyPyramid. Where are nuts located?
- How do we know how much of each food group we should eat? See the MyPyramid for Kids Poster (advanced version).

For More Nutritional Information, Visit:

http://www.mypyramid.gov.

As an Extension

1. *Distribute copies of the Making the Menu activity (Appendix B, page 137). Have the learners look at each food item in the "If you had …" section. They need to decide how many servings are in each of these foods. As they study the menu, ask them to fill in the number of circles that correspond to each food item. For example, the two whole wheat pancakes for breakfast would fill in two circles in the top row of the Bread, Cereal, Rice and Pasta group. The top row of circles represents the minimum number of recommended daily servings for each food group in the MyPyramid. The second row of circles represents the maximum number of recommended daily servings for each group. Explain that the top row of circles needs to be completely filled in, and encourage them to fill in as many of the circles as possible in the second row.*

The youths also can create a school menu. Go to Appendix B (page 138) and use the information from the recommended servings information (see Background Information) as a guide.

2. *Ask the group if beans are a vegetable or meat. Explain that beans are indeed a vegetable but can be used as a meat dish, too. Show them MyPyramid. Ask them to find the Vegetable Group and the Meat & Beans Group. If they are eating beans as a vegetable, how much should they eat? If they are eating beans instead of meat, how much should they eat? It is more or less? Why or why not? Explain that these types of meals are called "meatless meals." When eating a "meatless meal," a starch such as potatoes or rice needs to be added to make it a balanced meal. The combination of starch and beans/peas provides all the protein growing bodies need.*

Label Reader

Objective: To learn the importance of eating breakfast and how to make healthful food choices by using information found on food labels

Time: 45 minutes

Materials: Food Labeling page (Appendix B, pages 139); poster of a food label; samples of food labels from breakfast foods (such as cereal, breakfast bars, toaster pastries, fruit juice, eggs and milk); food labels of fresh fruits and vegetables, if available; (You may wish to send home the supplemental parental take-home sheets in Appendix C, Fruits and Vegetables: Nutritious and Delicious, page 157, and Nutrition Facts for Healthful Eating, page 159.)

Sample label for
Macaroni & Cheese

Nutrition Facts

Serving Size 1 cup (228g)
Serving Per Container 2

Amount Per Serving	
Calories 250	Calories from Fat 110

	% Daily Value*
Total Fat 12g	**18%**
Saturated Fat 3g	**15%**
Cholesterol 30mg	**10%**
Sodium 470mg	**20%**
Total Carbohydrate 31g	**10%**
Dietary Fiber 0g	**0%**
Sugars 5g	
Protein 5g	

Vitamin A	4%
Vitamin C	2%
Calcium	20%
Iron	4%

* Percent Daily Values are based on a 2,000 calorie diet. Your Daily Values may be higher or lower depending on your calorie needs:

	Calories:	2,000	2,500
Total Fat	Less than	65g	80g
Sat Fat	Less than	20g	25g
Cholesterol	Less than	300mg	300mg
Sodium	Less than	2,400mg	2,400mg
Total Carbohydrate		300g	375g
Dietary Fiber		25g	30g

Before the Lesson

Do you want to learn more about the foods you eat? Look no further than the Nutritional Facts panel on a food package. This label can be a wealth of information for determining the amount of energy, fat, and specific nutrients that is in a food. To better understand food labels, dissect a label into its different components:

Serving Size: This is the amount of a food that an average person might eat.

Servings Per Container: This is the number of servings that are in the package.

Calories: This is the amount of energy per serving.

Calories from Fat: This is the number of calories that come just from fat. To figure out the percentage of calories from fat, simply divide the calories from fat by the total number of calories per serving.

Example: Calories from Fat = 30
Calories per serving = 90

33 percent of the calories in a serving of this food are from fat.

% Daily Value: The numbers down the right side of the Nutrition Facts panel are the percentage of the recommended amount of energy and nutrients that are provided per serving. On most labels, the % Daily Value is based on a 2,000 calorie diet. People with higher or lower energy needs may need different amounts of some nutrients.

Cholesterol: A fat-like substance found in animal products.

Sodium: Often called salt. For some people, eating high amounts of sodium may lead to high blood pressure. Canned and processed foods often have higher amounts of sodium than unprocessed foods. Try to limit the amount of sodium in the diet to about 2 teaspoons of salt per day.

Total Carbohydrate: Carbohydrates are found in foods like bread, pasta, potatoes, fruits, and vegetables. Total carbohydrates include dietary fiber and sugars.

Dietary Fiber: Also called roughage. Choosing foods high in fiber can help lower risk for heart disease and cancer. To increase intake of fiber, consume whole grains, fruits and vegetables, and legumes.

Sugars: Includes natural sugars, such as those found in fruits, juices and milk products, and added sugars which are often found in candy and soda.

Protein: The body needs this nutrient for growth, repair of body tissues, and for general maintenance. Animal products like meat, milk and eggs along with some vegetable foods like grains and legumes give plenty of protein to meet human needs.

The lower part of the Nutrition Facts panel lets consumers know the amount of specific nutrients like vitamin A, vitamin C, calcium and iron that is found in a single serving of the food or beverage.

Vitamin A: Helps us see at night, is needed for bone and skin growth and development, and helps our body fight disease.
Vitamin C: Helps the body fight infections and heal wounds. May help prevent some diseases like cancer and heart disease.
Calcium: Promotes strong bones and teeth.
Iron: Helps carry oxygen throughout the body.

Interestingly, all food labels must list all the ingredients in descending order according to weight. At a glance, consumers are able to compare nutrient values. Ingredients in one cereal may be listed as sugar, corn, corn syrup. Ingredients for another cereal may be listed as corn, molasses, salt. The second cereal is more nutritious - it lists corn as the major ingredient, not sugar.

LET THE FUN BEGIN!

Ask the group members if they have ever heard the saying, "Breakfast is the most important meal of the day." Then have them tell you if they think this is true and, if so, why.

Next, ask them to tell you what makes a car run. The obvious answer should be gas or fuel. Ask what happens if you forget to put gas in the car. The car eventually runs out of gas and won't run anymore.

Explain that the word "breakfast" means "to break the fast." Think about the time from when a person goes to sleep to when that person wakes up the next morning. Point out that for some people that may be 6 to 10 hours or even longer. Even though the person was sleeping, the body was still working. As a result, the person's "fuel" or energy levels get low. Explain that if you don't refuel your body with food when you wake up, then you may be running on empty. Ask, "Does a car run on empty?" Ask them if they think a person can run on empty (maybe, but not very good).

Next, ask group members the following question: "What if I don't have any gas to put in the car? Can I put other things in the gas tank to get the car to run?" The answer is no. If you don't put the right fuel in the car, then the car won't run. Explain that people are a little bit different than cars because people can run on different types of fuel or food. Still, there are some types of fuel or food that help us run better than others.

Next show different types of foods that are commonly eaten at breakfast (cereal and milk, juice, eggs). Ask students the question: "If I have many different fuels to choose from, how can I decide which fuel helps my body run at its best?"

Pass out a copy of a food label and identify its components. Explain to the group that food labels help people know what they are eating. The labels tell us how much fuel and nutrition are found in the food. Have group members look at the percentages of each nutrient found on the label. The percentages tell us how much of a certain nutrient is found in a serving. Try to select foods that provide at least 10 percent of your daily needs of calcium, iron, vitamin A, vitamin C, and fiber. If you do this, over a day's time you are likely to meet the goal of 100 percent. Foods that contain fat, cholesterol and sodium have important roles in the body, but should be eaten less often and in smaller amounts.

Now, have group members look at the sample breakfast labels. Have them rank the labels from highest to lowest for each nutrient using the nutrient percent listed on the label.

At home, have members select two foods commonly found in their homes. Use the Food Labeling Page (Appendix B, page 139) to rank the foods in order from highest to lowest for each nutrient, based on the food labels. They should bring the rankings back to the next meeting to share with others.

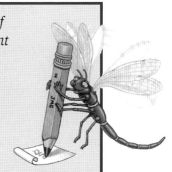

Which processed foods are good for you and your pocketbook? Gather a collection of different labels of foods products. Have learners compare the contents of the different labels between brands (brand name versus generic) and types of foods (baked versus fried). Use the following questions to help guide your group in a discussion:

Discussion Questions

1. Which ingredient is listed first?
2. Which is listed second?
3. Which product(s) is/are the better buy? Why?

Taste Test

Objective: To evaluate fruit based on color, texture, taste and smell
Time: 25 minutes
Materials: Fruits containing excellent sources of vitamin A and vitamin C (refer to Fruits and Vegetables: Nutritious and Delicious page 157), Taste Test (Appendix B, page 141), Vitamin A Helps Me See, Grow and Play (Appendix B, page 142), Vitamin C is Good for Me (Appendix B, page 143)

Before the Lesson

Fruits and vegetables are natural sources of vitamins A and C, which are two nutrients that may prevent some diseases, including cancer and heart disease.

In plants, vitamin A is called beta-carotene. Fruits and vegetables that are high in vitamin A are often dark green or orange in color. One serving of cantaloupe, broccoli, pumpkin, carrots, sweet potatoes, or mango contributes at least 20 percent of the recommended amounts of vitamin A, making these excellent sources of this nutrient.

For excellent sources of vitamin C, choose orange juice, honeydew melon, watermelon, pineapple, greens (turnip, mustard or collard), kiwi, strawberries, Chinese cabbage or papaya. A serving from any of these fruits or vegetables provides 20 percent or more of the recommended amounts of vitamin C.

Before beginning

Select five different fruits and cut into bite-sized chunks (have enough pieces for each student to sample each type). Store the fruit in five separate containers.
Refer to the table on page 157, Fruits and Vegetables: Nutritious and Delicious, for nutrient information.

LET THE FUN BEGIN!

Write the words color, texture, taste and smell on the chalkboard or poster. Tell students that they are going to evaluate several different fruits. Make sure learners understand each of the terms and how they are to rate the food. Explain that texture is how the fruit feels in their mouths and against their tongues. Ask them if they have ever eaten foods with a smooth texture and ask them to tell you an example. Do the same for crunchy, grainy, lumpy, sticky, and other textures you can think of.

Have five plates of different fruits, labeled A, B, C, D, E (do not name the fruit). Pass out the Taste Test page (Appendix B, page 141). Explain to learners that they should circle a number beside each characteristic to give each fruit a "grade." The number one is the lowest score and five is the highest value. After learners have finished tasting and rating each fruit, they should add up the scores to find which one had the highest ranking.

Let learners try to guess what each plate contained before you reveal it. Ask learners if any fruits were rated high that they did not know they liked.

As an Extension

Ask the group to rank the fruit samples in order from highest to lowest percentage for vitamins A and C, using the Vitamin C is Good for Me and Vitamin A Helps Me See, Grow and Play pages (Appendix B, pages 142-143). Use the table on Fruits and Vegetables: Nutritious and Delicious (page 157) for more information on nutrients. Your group can make comparisons between the values the fruits are given compared to nutrient values.

In the Classroom

Have students visit the Junior Master Gardener web page at *www.jmgkids.us* and click on Golden Ray Series Health & Nutrition from the Garden.

Challenge them to go on a hunt for the fruit or vegetable that contains the highest percentage of vitamin A.

Do the same for vitamin C, fiber and iron.

Rough and Tough Foods

Objective: To understand that dietary fiber comes from plants and to learn the role of fiber in good health

Time: 25 minutes

Materials: Sandpaper and smooth plastic or celery and apples, a zero fiber food, a good fiber food and an excellent fiber food (see below), colored paper, glue, Rough and Tough Foods (Appendix B, page 144), and How Much Fiber is Right for Me? (Appendix B, page 145), (You may wish to send home the supplemental parental take-home sheet in Appendix C, Feast on Fiber for Better Health, page 161.)

Before the Lesson

Fiber is a compound found only in fruits, vegetables and grain products. Dietary fiber is present in two forms: soluble and insoluble.

Soluble fiber: Forms a gel when it is mixed with a liquid. Lowers blood cholesterol levels which may lead to a reduced risk of heart disease. May help regulate blood sugar, which is especially important for people with diabetes.

Good Plant Sources: Oats, peas, beans, apples, oranges

Phyllium (silly-um): Another soluble fiber found in some cereal products.

Insoluble fiber: Also known as "roughage." Helps the body get rid of waste, cleans out the digestive tract and helps the intestines get rid of potentially harmful substances.

Good Plant Sources: Whole wheat foods, cauliflower, green beans, skins of fruits and root vegetables

Other Benefits: Foods high in fiber can aid in controlling weight since these foods are bulky and keep the stomach full without overeating.

Ways to Increase Fiber Intake: Include whole grains, fruits and vegetables in daily meals. Try to include peas and beans in meals twice each week. Be sure to drink plenty of fluids to help the body stay hydrated.

Daily Recommended Amount: Adults (age 20 and up): 25 grams; Children: age + 5 = grams of fiber

Before Beginning

Prepare fingerpaint foods using glass containers of

(1) blended sugar, cola or candy (no fiber)
(Recipe: 1 cup water and ½ cup sugar, blend for 15 seconds. Use warm water to dissolve faster.)

(2) celery, broccoli or apples with peels (good fiber source)
(Recipe: 1 cup broccoli and ½ cup water, blend for 45 sec.)

(3) whole wheat or bran flake cereal (excellent fiber source)
(Recipe: 1 cup all bran cereal and 1 cup water, blend 5 sec. Mix enough for each gardener to participate.)

(4) an unknown (see Fiber Options on next page)

LET THE FUN BEGIN!

Have the gardeners close their eyes. Tell them that you will have them rub their fingers across two mystery objects and that you want them to describe how each feels. Allow each gardener to feel the sandpaper and plastic (or use cut celery and apples). Ask them to open their eyes and describe what they felt.

Explain that these words describe the objects' texture. Texture means how something feels and ranges from fine to medium to coarse. Sometimes we know how something feels just by looking at it. Show the gardeners the objects and allow them to compare the fine texture to the coarse texture.

Explain that foods have textures called "fiber." Scientists say that the fiber we eat that comes from plants has many healthful benefits. The belief that "an apple a day keeps the doctor away" may be true because fruits and vegetables contain fiber. Fiber helps support the plant during its life cycle and helps support healthy bodies too. Fiber in the diet can help reduce the risk of cancer and heart disease. Think of fiber as a scrub brush for the body—it clears and cleans it out quick! Explain that you may not taste fiber, but you can feel it.

Have the gardeners look at each of the foods in the glass containers and make a guess as to which foods have no fiber, some fiber and the most fiber. Excellent sources for fiber are the "rough and tough" foods. Tell gardeners that eating foods that are high in fiber will help their bodies stay tough, too.

Next, describe what is in each of the known containers and have gardeners fingerpaint the different blended food fibers onto colored paper by sweeping the paper with their fingers several times to leave a thin coat of each mixture. Then show the "unknown" container and have them guess the food source. Try to match the color of the food with the paper color so that the colors blend together. The different food groups will have different degrees of texture. Have the gardeners then cut out their samples and glue them in the appropriate boxes on the Rough and Tough Foods page (Appendix B, page 144). Remind gardeners not to eat the food paints because they could be toxic, depending on the length of time between food paint preparation and use.

Foods that contain fiber sometimes have rougher texture and are usually thicker than foods that are lower in fiber. A banana is a good source of fiber that has little texture, but it is thick when mashed or blended. Foods high in fiber, such as wheat bran, also absorb water. Check your containers periodically to be sure the food paints are a usable consistency.

Fiber options

Excellent Source ≥5 grams/serving	Good Source 2.5 - 4.9 grams/serving	Zero Fiber 0 grams/serving
Dry beans and peas Whole wheat Whole wheat bran	Dried apricots Medium banana Medium apple w/peel Oatmeal Baked Potato w/skin	Apple Juice Smooth peanut butter Margarine Cola Eggs/meat/fish Poultry Pork Marshmallows Cheese

As an Extension

Include a food tray for gardeners to sample before beginning this activity. Include no fiber, good fiber source, and excellent fiber source for them to see and taste. Or compare the differences of dietary fiber in pureed apples, a commercially available applesauce and apple juice and discuss the differences.

In the Classroom

The recommended amount of fiber for children up to 20 years of age is "age + 5."

Have students determine their daily value of fiber for themselves, their brothers, sisters and parents using the How Much Fiber is Right for Me? page (Appendix B, page 145).

If your students are 8 years old, then the daily value of fiber would be 8 + 5 = 13 grams per day.

U-B the Judge

Objective: To compare taste, economic and aesthetic values of fresh, frozen and canned fruits and vegetables

Time: 45 minutes

Materials: Canned, frozen and fresh samples, U-B the Judge (Appendix B, page 146), scale (optional), and pencils

Before the Lesson

Many grocers use three factors when selecting produce for market: (1) quality of the produce (2) the quantity available, and (3) consistency of the grower. However, price most often overrides all of the above.

In choosing fresh produce from a local market, consider the following guidelines:

Look: Color often indicates the ripeness of fruits and vegetables. To determine this, you must know what color the produce should be. Also check for bruises and scars. Pick the fruit or vegetables with the best color and the least amount of blemishes or bruising, which can cause produce to spoil quicker and waste valuable space, time and money.

Smell: Some fruits will ripen after picking. As these fruits ripen, the sugar content continues to rise and the fragrance increases; the stronger the scent, the more ripe the fruit. This may be helpful with some fruits like peaches. If a fruit smells extremely sweet or smells sour it may be overly ripe.

Touch: Ripe fruits and vegetables should be firm to the touch but give under a little pressure. If the skin does not have any "give" or is too hard, it may not yet be ripe; if it is mushy and soft, it may be too ripe. When purchasing or picking, ripened fruits should be used the same day or preserved on the day of purchase for future use.

Season: Produce is often imported from states (such as: Texas, California, Florida) and other countries (such as: Central America and South America) in order to offer a variety of produce year-round. The freshest and best quality vegetables and fruits are those in season for your area.

Even though a fruit or vegetable is not perfect, it is still usable. Cut out the unusable portions with a clean knife. Unusable portions include disease, insect or wind damage. Clean the knife with soap and warm water before continuing to use it on that piece or another piece of produce. Always wash produce before cutting or eating.

> **Try to use samples...** based on what is currently growing in your groups' garden. This can help emphasize the economic advantage of growing fresh produce. Home gardens can save money, enhance aroma and flavors, and provide young people with a sense of accomplishment that helps build self-esteem.

LET THE FUN BEGIN! Discuss with the group the differences in preservation techniques for the three samples. Ask them to rank and compare the taste, price and appearance between produce fresh from the garden (or local market), canned, and frozen. Pass out "U-B the Judge" page (Appendix B, page 146) to each gardener to rate the sample types.

Let your learners become cooks. Divide them into three small groups and let each group make a fruit/berry cobbler using the following recipe. One group should use fresh fruit, one should use canned and one should use frozen fruit. Have members compare the three cobblers for price and taste.

Berry Cobbler

You'll need:

1 cup sugar	1 stick margarine
1 cup flour	cooking spray
1 cup milk	3 cups of fruit
½ tsp. salt	
1 ¼ tsp. baking powder	

Mix: Combine sugar, flour, salt, and baking powder. Add milk and mix well. Spray the bottom and sides of a 9 X 13 inch pan using cooking spray. Pour the dough into the pan and add the berries or other fruit evenly over the top of the dough mixture. Slice a stick of margarine over the fruit evenly. Bake in a low oven at 325 degrees F for 30 to 40 minutes, or until evenly browned. Remove from the oven and cool. If needed, sprinkle with granulated sugar before serving. *(Courtesy of Lenora Sebesta, Snook, Texas)*

Berries make an excellent example to use in this activity to compare costs. In most cases, ounce for ounce the price difference is greater for berries in comparison to other fresh fruits or vegetables. Berry samples include: blueberry, blackberry, strawberry, raspberry or dewberry. Whichever fruit you choose, it needs to be available as fresh, frozen and canned. Fresh berries are also available from local markets depending on the season and your area. Prepare samples of each type of fruit for the gardeners to judge its taste, appearance, price, and overall value. Make nutrition labels available for each presentation of fruit and calculate its price per ounce/pound.

If berries are lacking or are in need of care in your garden, the Pass Along Patch activity is a good community service project for your group to do to help future young gardeners in your area (Community Service and Leadership section, page 103).

fruit and Veggie Mania

Objective: To gain a familiarity with characteristics of common and exotic fruits and vegetables
Time: 30 minutes
Materials: Fruit and Veggie Mania cards (Following Acknowledgments in Appendix). These can be laminated for durability.

Ask the gardeners whether or not they take vitamins. Ask them why they think some people take vitamins. Explain that one reason people take vitamins is to give their bodies nutrients that they might not be getting from the foods they eat. Many people think that if they take vitamins, then they don't have to worry about what they eat. Explain that although taking vitamins can be helpful, the best way to get the nutrients the body needs is to eat a variety of foods. To help meet these needs, gardeners should eat at least five servings of fruits and vegetables each day.

Explain that they are going to play a game that will help them learn (1) nutrient amounts of certain fruits and vegetables, (2) how these fruits and vegetables grow, (3) the parts of the plant that are eaten, and (4) the edible colors of these foods (the color eaten).

Directions for Play

The game is designed for 2-4 players. Each gardener receives seven cards to start the game. The remaining cards are stacked in a pile face down in the area called the "pantry pile" on the game board. Explain to the group that the object of the game is to "eat" all of the fruit and veggie cards they can by playing the cards out of their hands. Once any player has played all of the cards in his/her hand, that gardener is the winner of the game.

A card may be played only if it has something in common with the card that was played before it. There are five ways a card can be in common with the previously played card; if both cards:

1. have the same fruit or vegetable on the faces of the cards, OR
2. have at least one nutrient amount that matches, OR
3. are the same plant part (leaf, stem, root, flower or fruit), OR
4. have the same growing season (cool season or warm season), OR
5. have one edible color in common.

If a player cannot play a card that matches the card showing, then that player must draw a card from the "Pantry Pile." If the drawn card is a match, the card is played; otherwise, the player loses his/her turn.

There are special cards that can be played. They are:

Pyramid Power Card: Can only be played when no cards in a player's hand have anything in common with the card just played. The gardener that plays this card chooses the fruit or veggie to resume play.

Pyramid Pop Card: Can be played at anytime. Allows a player to play two cards at one time. A player plays a card along with the Pyramid Pop card. The next player has to pick up the Pyramid Pop card and loses his/her turn. Play resumes with the fruit or vegetable card that is showing (the fruit or vegetable card played first by the Pyramid Pop card player).

Tasty Turn Around Card: Can be played at anytime. This card allows a player to switch the direction of play. For example, if players are playing in a clockwise direction, then players would start playing in a counter-clockwise direction.

Second Serving Card: Can be played at anytime. When this card is played, the next player must draw two cards from the Pantry Pile and loses his/her turn.

If all cards are drawn from the Pantry Pile before the game is over, cards that have been played should be reshuffled and put back into the Pantry Pile. When the game is over, ask the gardeners what new and surprising bits of information they learned about fruits and vegetables.

Explain to the group that the food items on the Pyramid Pop cards are foods located at the peak (or smallest portion) of the MyPyramid. These are items that should only be eaten in small amounts or eaten occasionally.

Tell the group it is important to remember that some of the most nutritious foods may be foods they don't eat often enough. Challenge them to try to eat, in the next few weeks, at least one fruit and one vegetable they played in the card game.

Discussion Questions

1. Which fruit or vegetable had the highest amount of vitamin A? vitamin C? fiber?
2. Name two fruits and their plant parts. Name two vegetables and the plant parts.
3. What are two root crops?

Beauty Contest

Objective: To rank fruits and vegetables based on appearance for maximum quality and nutrition

Time: 25 Minutes

Materials: Fresh vegetables, Blue Ribbon Fruits and Vegetables activity page (Appendix B, page 147)

Before Beginning

Put learners into groups of four and assign each group member to bring a particular vegetable to school on the day of this activity. One group might bring tomatoes, another group eggplant and so on. Or plan a trip to the local supermarket or farmer's market to give gardeners a much broader understanding of how to choose fresh fruits and vegetables. Gardeners need access to fresh whole vegetables and fruits in order to rank them on appearance.

LET THE FUN BEGIN!

Ask learners what they look for when they go to buy sneakers. Explain that most people look for certain things in a tennis shoe, such as a certain color or a certain style or because of the athlete who advertised the shoe.

Then turn the discussion to foods. Give examples of restaurants and ask for a show of hands of who has eaten there and why they chose to eat there. Then ask them if they have helped mom or dad pick fresh fruits and vegetables when shopping? If so, inform them that they probably decided whether or not to buy the vegetable based on how it looked, too.

Explain that their job is to judge the fresh vegetables and fruits. Separate produce into groups by variety. Ask gardeners to rank the items within each group. Allow gardeners to pick up and examine the fruits and vegetables before ranking.

After they rank the produce and choose a blue ribbon winner for each variety, they should fill out the Blue Ribbon Fruits and Vegetable (page 147). Ask them to identify the fruit or vegetable, draw it and give the reason(s) for choosing it over the others. They might state that one was larger, had better color, had fewer blemishes or other criteria. Once everyone has decided on the ranking, have each gardener share his or her decision with the rest of the group to see if all agreed. Those who came to a different conclusion should explain their criteria, and the group should decide together on an order. Have members from each group tell friends and families about their blue ribbon vegetable or fruit.

As an Extension

Include overripe fruits and have gardeners rank these items. Explain that some fruits and vegetables may not be attractive but are good to eat even if they are overripe. An example is overripe bananas. These bananas usually cost less than regular bananas and make really good breads or muffins, and they freeze well too. A bargain today can last for several months if properly frozen.

Healing Power

Objective: To understand the potential healing powers of the plant kingdom

Time: First meeting—15 minutes; Second meeting—45 Minutes

Materials: Pen, paper, Tree of Knowledge page (Appendix B, page 148), guest speaker (optional), disposable camera (optional), The Shaman's Apprentice by Mark J. Plotkin

Before the Lesson

IT IS IMPORTANT to stress to children that plants contain naturally occurring compounds that have the ability to heal or harm. Stress to your group to NEVER use or eat a plant that is unfamiliar or to use it in any way other than its intended use.

Always check with your family physician prior to taking any new medications or supplements.

This activity is an opportunity to present the idea that plants may be used in numerous healthful ways, in addition to dietary purposes. Presenting this idea to your group will give them an opportunity to brainstorm, preserve a little history, and offer opportunities for cross- and intergenerational mentoring. As each new generation comes into adulthood, much of this information is lost.

Plants have existed for millions of years and have been useful to man in many ways. Throughout time, people have used plants to help heal and prevent sickness and infections, and used herbs to add flavor and nutrients to foods and teas and to reduce offensive odors.

Early man depended on plants to supplement the diet and used plants in medicinal ways to help stay healthy and heal the sick. In Victorian times, people wore sachets made from plant flora to mask body odor between bathes. Today, many everyday household items and pharmaceuticals are derived from plants. Below are examples of some more common plant uses:

Aloe Vera:	Helps heal minor burns
Camphor:	Cold medicines
Chamomile:	Herb used in teas to help to settle nerves and upset stomach
Citrus:	Fruit used as fragrance
Menthol:	Cold medicines
Rosemary:	Herb used as a spice to add flavor
Willow:	Aspirin
Yaupon:	Used by early Indians to induce vomiting

Scientists are able to copy plant compounds and create synthetic prescription and nonprescription drugs. Many of these curative compounds are found in plants of South America's rainforest. This is one reason the rainforest is so important to life. Each day rainforest acreage is being destroyed, and we loose a virtual warehouse of plants with healing compounds that scientists have yet discover.

LET THE FUN BEGIN!

At the first meeting, ask for a show of hands to indicate how many gardeners know of someone who has used a plant to help heal a cut. Explain that even before Columbus came to America people used plants as medicine to help make them well. Plants have been used to heal wounds, soothe a stomachache, and even battle diseases inside our bodies. Ask each member to visit a grandparent, great-grandparent or elderly neighbor and discuss ways that person has used plants to help a sick friend or family member.

Have each gardener make a list of the plants mentioned in their conversations, using the Tree of Knowledge page (Appendix B, page 148) and bring the list to the next meeting. To make this time more memorable, encourage gardeners to take pictures with the person they have interviewed (optional). Some students may not have grandparents that live close to them. If so, plan a group visit to a retirement center, nursing home or other elderly care facility.

At the next meeting, ask each gardener to share the list of plant names. You can write these on the board or poster board. Some gardeners may have many plants to share with the group, while others may have only one or two. As each plant is repeated, make a mark to show how well it is known for its healing powers.

Discuss with the group how it is possible that plants help heal cuts or fight infection. You may want to invite a speaker, such as a Master Gardener, plant breeder or botanist, to visit with the group and speak about the medicinal uses of plants.

You can explain that some plants have certain natural chemicals to protect themselves from insects, diseases and even other plants. Plants have the ability to store these protective chemicals in different parts, whether it's the flower, fruit, stem, leaf, root or bark. When used in different products, these chemicals may help fight off harmful germs and help keep our bodies strong and healthy. Willow bark is used to make aspirin; menthol and camphor are used to make cold medicines, and chamomile tea may help settle nerves and upset stomach. Aloe plants are used on minor burns. Keep in mind that the difference between a medicine and a toxin can be the dosage amount.

In the Classroom

Read the children's book *The Shaman's Apprentice* by Mark J. Plotkin, Ph.D. to the group.

Dr. Plotkin tells of his true adventures in the Amazon rain forest learning from a tribe their usage and knowledge of healing plants.

Your group can learn about the history of the rain forest, information and traditions passed from generation to generation, and the importance of the plant world.

As a group, make a Tree of Knowledge book. In this book, gardeners can record the history of the group's personal interviews. It can be filled with pictures, interview sheets, recommended readings, group passages and other interesting fun-filled facts.

Discussion Questions:

1. What is a desert? A forest? A rain forest?
2. In what part of the world is the rain forest located?
3. What are some plants that people use to help them stay healthy?
4. What other living things can people use to stay healthy? (fungi and bacteria)

Teaching Concept 6

Healthful Snacks

Stop! Why are you offering potato chips as a snack? Instead offer young gardeners Strip Chips made of sweet potatoes and made crisp in the microwave. Children can learn to snack in more healthful, nutritious ways and may be more willing to try new and different foods grown in their own gardens. Gardening friends and leaders can offer a support system, providing comfortable environments in which your gardeners can experience different foods and healthful snacks. Younger gardeners may exhibit some hesitation, but with a little encouragement and examples from leaders and peers, they'll soon join in the fun, too.

Gardeners will learn and experience healthful snack alternatives to help keep them energized and active.

ACTIVITIES

Fruit and Veggie Lab, Apple Surprise, Symmetry Snacks II
Robust Rainbow Recipes, Strip Chips, Junk Food Blues
More Snack-time Fun

Did You Know?

Early civilizations left evidence that food was used to prevent and cure many illnesses. Today, scientists are beginning to evaluate and understand the naturally occurring compounds found in plants and the health benefits for humans. Plants contain compounds called "phytochemicals" (fight-o-chemicals: phyto means plant, chemicals means compounds) that are naturally occurring and are believed to help the human body in the prevention of, or protection against, diseases such as cancer, heart disease and stroke.

Phytochemicals, sometimes called antioxidants, can be further broken down into specific natural plant compounds that are believed to help prevent or protect against certain cancers and other diseases. However, not all phytochemicals protect against disease.

Researchers are also looking at the levels of phytochemicals in different varieties of fruits and vegetables and they are researching how to improve the nutrient content of plant-derived foods. Some researchers use a selective breeding program where a fruit or vegetable variety is continuously bred to produce a stable product that has a desired trait. Researchers also use gene manipulation to introduce one or two genes that control a desired trait into a different plant so it will show or express the desired trait.

Snack time offers a chance for youths to enjoy naturally sweet fast foods–fresh fruits and vegetables. Youths may be more willing to try new and different garden foods if they are with friends, peers and group leaders in a garden environment where they receive support and encouragement from one another. So, give your participants quick and easy recipes using fruits and vegetables from their garden. Food gardens can offer fast, fresh and nutritious snacks ... just pick 'em, wash 'em, eat 'em and go!

Fruits naturally produce chemical compounds and sugars, and contain vitamin A and vitamin C, along with many other nutrients. Activities in this chapter focus on the nutrients vitamin A, vitamin C, calcium and iron those nutrients listed on food labels as mandated by the U.S. government.

Vitamin C *is a water-soluble nutrient and some of its vitamin content can be lost during the washing and cooking processes.*

Vitamin A *is fat-soluble vitamin. Since fat-soluble vitamins do not interact with water, the nutrient value is usually retained during washing and cooking.*

Storage after Harvest

Properly processing fresh vegetables and fruits helps prevent loss of valuable nutrient content. Fruits and vegetables from the garden should be processed within 2 hours after picking. Although severed from the parent plant, respiration and enzymatic activities continue inside picked fruit or vegetables. Place harvested food items in the refrigerator to slow these internal activities before processing. Refrigerators also can be used as temporary storage.

Remember, overcooking can diminish nutrient value of fresh fruits and vegetables.

Most nutrient content

Fresh

Baked/Steamed

Blanched

Boiled

Least nutrient content

LEFTOVERS

Leftovers can be stored in airtight, resealable bags or containers and placed in the refrigerator. For longer storage, store leftovers in the freezer. See ABC's of Healthful Eating (Teaching Concept 5) for additional information.

Other activities that could be used to support this teaching concept are Safety First (page 52), Party Confetti Salad (page 57), Beauty Contest (page 81), Garden to the Table (page 53), Protection by Diversity (page 28), Bold Molds (page 55), Save It (page 58).

fruit and Veggie Lab

Objective: To learn what a fruit is and how to explore the difference between technical definitions and social customs

Time: 1 hour

Materials: A variety of produce, including an assortment of fruits and vegetables, paper plates, knife for leader to use in cutting produce

Ask children to name all of the vegetables they know, and write the names on the board or on a chart. Make a second list of all the fruits they know. Be sure to include the tomato on one of the lists. Ask children how they know which product is a fruit and which is a vegetable.

In botanical terms, a fruit is the reproductive part of the plant that develops from the ovary of a flower and produces seeds. These seeds will produce the next generation of plants. Many plant parts that we eat and commonly call "vegetables" are really fruits.

A true vegetable is a food product that comes from any part of the plant other than the flower, such as the roots (carrots and radishes), developing shoots (asparagus), stems (celery), or leaves (cabbage and lettuce).

After this discussion, select a sample of produce and ask the children what part of the plant it is and if it is a fruit or vegetable in botanical terms. (If you can cut it open and see seeds inside, as with tomatoes, cucumbers, squash, and eggplant, it is a fruit. If there are no seeds inside, it comes from a part of the plant other than the flower, and is a true vegetable.)

Tell children that when they eat broccoli and cauliflower, they are actually eating unopened flower buds. So, what are broccoli and cauliflower: fruit, vegetable or something in between?

On the vegetable chart, make a mark by all of the vegetables listed that are really fruits. The children may be surprised at the number of "fruits" they eat, botanically speaking. When all of the produce has been labeled, cut it up and serve as snacks while you lead the follow-up discussion below.

Follow-up Discussion

There are actually several different explanations used to separate fruits from vegetables. Fruit and vegetable growers distinguish the two by how the crop is grown. Vegetables are annual crops, which means the crop is planted, grown, and harvested all in 1 year, and are planted in rows in the fields. Fruits are perennial crops, which means that they grow and produce fruit over many years, rather than just one, and grow on bushes, vines, ground covers and trees.

Another explanation of the difference between fruits and vegetables is based on when then the item is eaten. According to social custom, vegetables are food items eaten with a main meal, while fruits are sweet treats to be eaten for dessert. Therefore, tomatoes, squash, and eggplants are vegetables because they are eaten as part of the main meal.

The discussion of fruits versus vegetables went to the Supreme Court in 1893! The case concerned tomatoes. As vegetables, they were taxed at a lower rate than fruits, which were considered a luxury item. The Supreme Court apparently thought that social customs were more important than botanical distinctions, because they decided that tomatoes were vegetables. The line between fruits and vegetables has been fuzzy ever since.

The exact time and reason why many fruits began to be called vegetables is unclear; but one thing is for sure, there are a lot of fruits masquerading as vegetables on our dinner tables! Tell children that the next time someone tells them to eat their veggies, they may need to look again to see whether they are really fruits!

Ask each child to eat a variety of fruits and vegetables at meals and snack times over the next few days.

Apple Surprise

Objective: To make a healthful, nutritious fruit snack alternative
Time: 1 hour
Materials: Four to five varieties of apples: Red Delicious, Granny Smith, Gala, Golden Delicious, Washington, Jonathan, Fuji, etc.; knife; plates; (You may wish to send home the supplemental parental take-home sheet in Appendix C, Apples: A Fast Food From Mother Nature, page 163.) *Snack items:* Apples, cinnamon, nutmeg, brown sugar, melon baller or butter knife, oven and baking sheet

Before the Lesson

Apples, like other fruits, are nutritious and often are an inexpensive snack food option for people "on the go." Think of apples as one of the original fast foods–pick it, wash it, eat it and go!

Apples fit in the fruit section of MyPyramid. Kids should eat 1½ cups of fruit each day.

Apples differ in color and texture. Some varieties are better than others for snacks, salads, and desserts.

APPLE VARIETIES

Red Delicious: Bright to dark red, sometimes with stripes. Has been bred for its shape. Great for use in salads, garnishes, fruit trays and snacks.

Golden Delicious: Golden to light yellow-green; skin is tender. Often called the "all purpose" cooking apple. Great for baking or eating raw.

Granny Smith: Bright to light green. Great for snacking, pies or for use in salads.

Gala: Yellow-orange under red striping to almost solid red striping to almost solid red. Great snack food!

Braeburn: Ranges from greenish-gold with red sections to almost solid red. Great choice for salads and snacks.

Jonagold: Color is a combination of Jonathan and Golden Delicious apples. Has a yellow-green base and a blush stripe. Great for eating fresh or for cooking.

LET THE FUN BEGIN!

Apples are usually available from the market all year around. Your choice in apples will depend on whether a tart, sweet, soft or crunchy apple is desired. Have an apple taste test to determine which apples are preferred and which will make the best Apple Surprise (recipe on the following page).

COMPARING APPLES TO APPLES

This activity can be used in conjunction with the Rough and Tough Foods activity (page 75) to reinforce what gardeners have learned about dietary fiber. Apples contain dietary fiber and vitamin C. If your gardeners have completed the Rough and Tough Foods activity, ask them to recall what they learned.

Dietary fiber only comes from plant materials and it helps our bodies digest food, acts as a scrub brush inside the body (scrubs out our digestive system), and may help fight against some cancers. Tell the gardeners that there is no one magical food that supplies every nutrient the body needs. A variety of foods will help supply the body with most of the vitamins and minerals needed for good energy and growth. That's why it is important to eat a variety of five servings of fruits and vegetables each day.

Ask the gardeners if they have eaten apples during the summer, during the spring, in the fall, or during the winter months. Most apples varieties are available year round. This is because apples will store for long periods of time if stored properly. In the refrigerator, apples will keep up to 3 weeks if conditions are favorable.

APPLE SAMPLINGS

1. Select four to five varieties of apples.

2. Display samples of each variety and label them A, B, C, D, E.

3. Be sure to thoroughly wash hands and apples, then peel and slice apples into wedges and arrange on paper plates by apple variety.

3. Label them 1, 2, 3, 4, 5.

3. Remember to record the variety of apple and its assigned number and letter. It may be helpful to write the apple variety on the bottom of the paper plate and arrange the tasting samples randomly.

4. Display and tasting samples should not correspond to one another; or A should be a different variety from 1.

5. Remind gardeners to practice food safety before handling the apple wedges wash hands with soap and warm water.

Send your gardeners on a mission. Explain that on this mission they need to find the best tasting apple available. Begin by asking gardeners to vote for their favorite apple on display. Gardeners will select one variety over the others based on appearance. Record responses on the Taste Test page (Appendix B, page 141-143).

Ask participants to sample at least one apple slice from each plate. They should then rank the different apple varieties according to category found on the Taste Test (page 141-143). Don't let them know which apples are which until everyone has had a chance to rank the varieties and has completed the activity sheet.

Gardeners may be amazed at which apple they thought they liked and which one(s) they really liked.

Apple Surprise Recipe

Cut off the top of the apple; this becomes the cap of the apple. Core the apple with a melon baller or butter knife. Be sure to remove the seeds and papery sheath. A smaller utensil leaves more apple to eat! Place the cored apple on a baking sheet and fill the center hole with brown sugar. Spread butter across the top of the apple. If you like, sprinkle cinnamon and nutmeg over the butter. Place the apple cap on top. Bake in an oven for 35 to 50 minutes at 350 degrees F or until the apple is soft. The length of time will vary depending on the apple type.

Caution: Be careful when removing the apple cap. It could be hot!

In the classroom

Give learners the price per pound of each type of apple. Based on the price per pound have them determine which apple is the least expensive and which is the most expensive. Then have them compare the price per pound to the physical size of each apple. Is the highest priced apple still the most expensive for the amount of apple bought? If not, which variety is? Is the least expensive apple still the most inexpensive for the amount of apple bought? If not, which variety is?

Symmetry Snacks II

Objective: To make a fun, healthful snack alternative and learn more about the insect world
Time: 45 minutes
Materials: Graham cracker, peanut butter or yogurt, two or three fresh fruits (i.e. strawberries, blueberries, kiwi, raisins), MyPyramid for Kids Poster (large enough for youths to see), masking tape

Call on a gardener to be a model. Use masking tape to create a center line on the volunteer. Ask gardeners to notice that it divides the body in half lengthwise. The human body and an insect's body are both symmetrical (have a mirror image). Ask gardeners to name symmetrical insects they have seen. Ask them to distinguish each insect as a beneficial or a harmful insect.

Pass out needed ingredients to each gardener to make their bug snack. Have members cut larger fruits into small bite-size pieces and choose an insect to create. It can be a beneficial or pest insect. Ask your group to be sure the snack insects are symmetrical. Remind them to draw an imaginary line down the middle of the insect's body. Each side will be a mirror-image of the other side; where there is a leg on one side of its body, there will be a leg in exactly the same place on the other side. Have gardeners create a bug snack that is symmetrically decorated, using graham crackers covered with peanut butter or yogurt and decorated with small pieces of different colored fresh fruits.

Remind garderners that insects have 3 body regions, 1 pair of antennae, 3 pair of legs, and can be with wings or without.

Try to use products from the garden, if possible or have the group make the peanut butter (instructions provided on page 98).

Explain that some foods may be more healthful than others in helping our bodies grow and stay healthy. Dissect a beneficial bug snack and ask gardeners to place each item in the appropriate food group: graham crackers fall in the Grains and Cereal Group, fresh fruit or vegetables fall in their own groups, yogurt is in the Dairy Group, peanut butter is in the Meat Group, etc. When the group has finished making their bugs and the discussion is complete, let them "bug out" and enjoy the treats!

As an Extension

Begin the lesson by having the gardeners make their own peanut butter, and consider letting gardeners make several snacks using the peanut butter they have made. The Better Butter recipe and Ants on a Log recipe can both be found on page 98.

In the classroom

Have students write a "how to" paper on making peanut butter. Then ask someone to read aloud their instructions on how to make peanut butter. As each part is read, literally do the instruction. An example might be "take some salt"; the leader takes three grains of salt and adds to the peanut butter. Students quickly understand the power of words and how to better communicate with one another.

Robust Rainbow Recipes

Objective: To understand that plants have naturally occurring compounds that benefit the body by using five fruits to create a robust snack
Time: 45 minutes
Materials: Five different colored fruits or vegetables

What are phytochemicals?

Phytochemicals are chemical components that occur naturally in plants, and are neither vitamins nor minerals. Plants are composed of many different chemicals. Some are responsible for functions such as flavor, aroma, plant structure and storage of nutrients.

Phytochemicals have been associated with the prevention and/or treatment of cancer, diabetes, cardiovascular disease and hypertension, among other diseases, in humans. Not all phytochemicals protect against disease, however.

It is difficult for children to imagine that they ever will be affected by chronic illness. However, a majority of children will have a loved one parent, grandparent, other family member or friend that will be diagnosed with one of these diseases. More than 77,000 new cases of cancer are diagnosed annually.

Scientists are evaluating plant chemicals and the roles they play in health and nutrition. It is known that most phytochemicals are families of chemicals. Not all family members do the same thing; one family member may help prevent disease while another may not.

Since fruits and vegetables are low in fat and rich in fiber, consuming a diet with plenty of these foods may decrease the risk of cancers and other chronic diseases. Currently, most children eat fewer than three servings of fruits and vegetables a day. Help start youths on the path to a long and healthy life by encouraging them to garden, harvest and eat what they have grown. Good health and nutritional habits start at a young age.

For additional information on phytochemical research, visit the Vegetable and Fruit Improvement Center Web site http://vic.tamu.edu

SIMPLE WAYS TO INCREASE FRUIT AND VEGETABLE INTAKE

Most of us do not eat the amount of fruit and vegetables our bodies need. To increase fruit and vegetable intake:

1. Snack on fresh fruit or raw vegetables.
2. Add strawberries, peaches or bananas to breakfast cereals or oatmeal.
3. If you have a choice between 100 percent juice or soda, pick the juice.
4. Brighten up salad with carrots, bell peppers, broccoli and cauliflower.
5. Add grapes and slices of apples and pears to a chicken salad.
6. A great topping for broiled meat, chicken or fish is salsa. One-half cup of salsa is equal to one serving of vegetables.

LET THE FUN BEGIN!

Remind gardeners of the Safety First activity (Teaching Concept 4, page 52) and ask them to say and demonstrate the safety rules before beginning.

Tell them they are going to make a robust rainbow recipe using five different colored fruits picked from the garden or local market. Or the group might create a vegetable stir-fry using fresh vegetables from the garden. Items can also be brought from home or donated by local merchants. Mention that these fresh items are some of the original fast foods: pick 'em, wash 'em, eat 'em and go!

Ask gardeners to name the colors of the rainbow red, orange, yellow, green, blue, indigo and violet. What other things are colorful? Plants are colorful too. Fruit makes colorful snacks and is healthful to eat.

Fruits come in a robust rainbow of colors and they contribute to a healthful diet because they are packed with more than just vitamins and minerals! Fruits contain natural compounds call phytochemicals that you can see, taste or smell. Think about the red color in a watermelon or the orange color of a carrot. Have you ever thought about what gives some onions that hot and spicy flavor? Or, have you ever smelled a strawberry?

Scientists are beginning to evaluate the compounds that plants make naturally and have a better understanding of how they help us. Use the following list of colors and the natural plant compounds that benefit us, and discuss with your gardeners.

Red: May help fight some cancers; helps fight colds; helps keep the heart healthy; and helps us see at night.

Orange: May help fight colds; aids in developing a healthy heart; may help prevent cataracts; acts as a scrub brush for inside the body (cleans out the digestive system).

Yellow: Aids in scrubbing out the body and may help prevent hypertension.

Green: May help fight some cancers; helps prevent cramps of legs and arms; helps us see at night; acts as a scrub brush for inside the body (cleans the digestive system).

Blue(berry): May help fight some cancers; may help prevent hypertension.

Purple: May help fight some cancers; helps develop red, strong blood that carries oxygen from the lungs.

Fruits have naturally occurring sugars, too, that are a good source of energy.

To make the salad, divide the gardeners into five small groups, one for each color used. Help the gardeners cut up each offering to be added to the snack. Cut bite-size pieces and toss them into the bowl. A glass container will allow gardeners to see the robust rainbow of colors. Begin with the color red, share its health benefits and naturally occurring compound. Follow this with the remaining four colors (orange, yellow, green, blue, indigo or violet) selected, piling one color on top of the other to create a rainbow. Once the fruits/vegetables are cut, ask a volunteer to toss the entire salad. Cooks can top the fruit snack with whipped cream, yogurt, etc.

AS AN EXTENSION

Use this activity with your gardeners as an opportunity to address sharing and cooperation among peers, family and communities. Read stories to your group that focus on sharing and learning to cooperate, such as *Stone Soup* by Marcia Brown or *Growing Vegetable Soup* by Lois Ehlert.

DISCUSSION QUESTIONS:

1. What types of fruits did you use?
2. Which one do you think has the sweetest flavor?
3. Which one has the tartest flavor?
4. Which fruit had the reddest color?
5. What is the advantage of eating a variety of fruits and vegetables rather than one fruit and one vegetable? (combination of many different vitamins, minerals and naturally occurring plant compounds.)

In the Classroom

Ask learners to name each color of the rainbow. Learners may or may not know each and every color. How can these colors be easily remembered? Explain that they can use the acronym "ROY G. BIV" to help them remember the colors of the rainbow and the order each appears: R = red, O = orange, Y = yellow, G = green, B = blue, I = indigo, V = violet. Then ask them to create a picture-story including a rainbow and the character "ROY G. BIV." The pictures can later be hung around the room for all to share and enjoy.

Strip Chips

Objective: To practice a quick, safe storage method for sweet potatoes by making Sweet Potato Chips

Time: 30 minutes

Materials: Sweet potato, potato peeler, microwave, salt (optional)

DISCUSSION QUESTIONS:

1. Have you eaten potato chips within the last few days?
2. How are potato chips cooked?
3. Where in MyPyramid does oil and fat fall?
4. Should these foods be eaten often or sometimes?

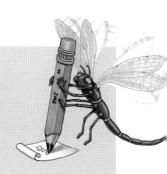

Explain that potatoes are a healthful food but, as with all foods, the way they are prepared can make them less healthful. When potatoes are deep fried in oil (as in preparing potato chips and french fries), they become a high fat food that we shouldn't eat as often. Ask group members what makes chips so popular (tastes good, crispy, salty, etc.). Challenge them to think of a homemade, more nutritious way to make chips. Explain that chips can be made in ways that will allow us to eat them more often. Have members spend some time discussing other ways chips can be prepared.

Tell them that they are going to prepare a potato chip snack in a fast, fun and very nutritious way. The first thing they should know is that they will not use an ordinary potato. Hold up a sweet potato. Ask the group if they have ever eaten one. Have them guess which potato is more nutritious. The gardeners might be surprised to know that the sweet potato is more nutritious because one serving contains all of the vitamin A their bodies need in a day and is a good source of vitamin C (1/3 of their daily need). Explain that you can tell that the sweet potato is more nutritious by just looking, because fruits and vegetables that are more colorful usually contain a greater amount of certain nutrients.

Next tell them the second way they will make the snack more nutritious is not to fry it in oil. Instead, it will be dehydrated in the microwave! Tell the gardeners that there is a very special tool that they will use to make the chips. Dehydrated potatoes must be sliced very thin so all of the moisture can be pulled from the potato. Have gardeners guess what the special tool is that can make thin slices. Hold up the potato peeler. Show them that this simple tool is perfect for quickly making thin slices.

Have gardeners practice the food safety rules—wash hands and foods. Show the group how to use the peeler to remove the skin. Explain how to use a peeler: lay the potato in the hand to hold it from the bottom. Then from the top, long side, use the peeler to cut off strips. Cut in the direction away from the hand and body. Take turns peeling strips of potato.

Have the gardeners lay a piece of plastic wrap over a paper plate. The strips should be laid in a single layer on the top of the plastic. The strips may then be sprinkled lightly with salt, if desired. Microwave on high for 2 to 4 minutes or until crisp. Turn the plate one-quarter turn every 20 seconds until done. Some of the thinner parts of the strips may brown as the chips are being cooked. Chips or parts that become too brown can be discarded.

Allow chips to cool. Serve immediately. Store uneaten chips in an airtight container.

In the Classroom

Have students make predictions and record information about the weight and volume of their chip strips. Have them weigh a potato before it has been stripped and dehydrated, then have them predict how heavy the chips will be. The chips can be weighed again. Students will be surprised by how much weight is lost once the water is removed. Have them also predict how much raw potato it will take to produce a cup of chip strips.

Junk Food Blues

Objective: To learn a rhythm to understand the benefits of eating nutritious, healthful snacks

Time: 20 minutes

Materials: Junk Food Blues song sheet (Appendix B, page 149)

BEFORE THE LESSON

MyPyramid reflects the recommendations established by the USDA to help Americans get their recommended daily allowance of vitamins and minerals and promotes disease prevention. Chips, candies and other similar products are "okay" to eat once in a while, but not every day.

Snack time offers a perfect time for Americans of all ages to include and meet the minimum number of five recommended daily servings of fruits and vegetables. Fresh fruits and vegetables are a part of a healthful eating plan that helps provide nutrients the body needs to be physically active.

Ask the students if they have heard the term junk food. Have them share their thoughts of what kinds of foods that come to mind when they hear that term. Point out that many foods have very little nutritional value or may contain high amounts of fats, oils or sugars. Although we can eat these types of foods occasionally, they should not be a regular part of a healthy diet. These foods do not provide our bodies with the proper nutrition or the needed "fuel" for our minds and bodies.

Then, introduce and have your group practice the Junk Food Blues song. Sing the song first so the students can pick up the rhythm. Then have the students join in.

Follow with a second discussion. Discuss and list the foods the child in the song ate in one column. Then discuss and list more healthful food substitutes in a second column. Allow participants to see and compare the two columns. You can also challenge them to create additional verses incorporating the healthful food substitutes. Perform the new version of the song before other groups of gardeners.

Junk Food Blues

I had a big hunger, wanted a tasty treat.
 Grabbed some soda and chips—started to eat
I ate the whole bag of chips, drank a can of soda, too.
 Now I ache somethin' awful—I got the low-down junk food blues.

Chorus:
I'm tired, my stomach hurts, my head and body ache.
 I'm eatin' too much junk food, too many fries and sugar flakes.
Now I want some good food—something my body really needs.
 Payin' attention to what I eat—each time before I feed.

Now I forgot my own song, when I fixed today's lunch.
 I packed some nachos, cookies and candy bar that crunched.
Same thing happened when I ate, 'cause healthy food I did not choose.
 I got that achy, tired feelin'—the low-down junk food blues.

Repeat chorus

Gotta big game today, playing the Mighty Bears.
 Eatin' some candy, lots of sugar, my plan to get prepared.
Wanna be fast and win against this other guy named Fred.
 But the candy didn't work, I lost, my face is sweaty and red.

Repeat chorus

The game was over and they had won, they were happy but I felt sick.
 Saw Fred munchin' on some grapes and some orange carrot sticks.
Then I knew it was my fault, I finally got a clue,
 'Cause all the junk that I ate before, gave me the low-down junk food blues.

Second Discussion Guidelines:

1. Why might the song's athlete run out of energy? (could have chosen more nutritious foods)
2. What other foods could the athlete have eaten instead? (fruits, vegetables or grain-based food products)
3. Do you think the athlete would have had more energy if he had eaten grapes or carrot sticks? (probably)

In the Classroom

Divide gardeners into smaller groups and have them discuss different foods for energy including those mentioned in the singsong above.

Your gardeners can discuss other foods that might be more appropriate to eat before a sporting event for needed energy.

More Snack-time Fun!

Use the following recipes to enhance or extend your group's gardening experience.

A Better Butter

You'll need: 2 cups roasted peanuts (shelled)
2 tablespoons of peanut oil
¼ cup sugar
1 teaspoon of salt (optional)

Mix peanuts, oil and dry ingredients in a blender and blend until smooth. A potato masher works well too. For crunchy peanut butter, add another ¼ cup of peanuts and blend a few seconds more. Use immediately or temporarily store in a refrigerator.

Jammin' Juice

You'll need: 2 cups of fruit juice
1 banana
1 peach
1 cup of water
ice cubes to taste
Sherbert or yogurt to taste

Mix and blend all of the ingredients in a blender until smooth. Makes enough for two or three people. You can also try blending any fruit or juice to make your own special favor!

Ants on a Log

You'll need: Celery
Peanut butter
Raisins

Clean and cut the celery into smaller pieces. Each celery piece is a log. Spread the peanut butter inside the hollow portion of the celery. Add the ants or raisins on top of the peanut butter to form a row.

Magical Fruit Salad

You'll need: 1 can (20 ounces) pineapple chunks, canned in natural juice
½ pound seedless grapes (use purple grapes for extra color)
2 bananas
1 cup low-fat milk
1 small package (3 ½ ounces) instant lemon or vanilla pudding mix OR sugarfree variety
Makes 15 servings

First, chill fruit. Wash and dry the grapes. Peel and cut up the bananas into bite-size pieces. Drain the can of pineapple chunks. Put pineapple, grapes and bananas into a bowl. Save the juice from the pineapple to drink later if you wish. Then pour the milk over the fruit. Slowly stir the mixture and sprinkle in the pudding mix. Stir until well blended. Let the mixture stand for 5 minutes to set.

Gardeners will enjoy watching the pudding rise, as if by "magic." Now, is a good time to eat your Magical Fruit Salad because it is best if eaten immediately.

Note: Any combination of fresh, frozen or canned fruits can be used.

Source: ENP program, Texas AgriLife Extension Service, Texas A&M University System

Life Skills and Career Exploration

The world of work has changed dramatically over the past decade. Technology plays an increasingly vital role in the workplace and makes it a challenge to keep current with constant changes.

Workers need to be problem solvers who can integrate science-based, mathematical, written and oral skills into the workplace with a creative flare. The structure of work has become more complex: Teams are becoming an increasingly important component of the workplace. In short, young gardeners need exposure and opportunities to learn skills that will enable them to succeed in rapidly changing, technological, team-oriented, work environments.

The Possibilities

Objective: To understand one technique scientists use in developing new plant varieties
Time: 30 minutes
Materials: The Possibilities page (Appendix B, page 150), blue and brown markers, pencils

Name different physical traits or characteristics of learners, such as brown hair, blue eyes, round face. Why do you suppose everyone is different?

Explain that this is because in the cells of our bodies there are long, tiny strings. (The strings are very tiny but can be seen with a high-powered microscope.) On the strings are codes or "genes" that tell cells what to do or how an animal or plant will look. One code comes from the father and one code comes from the mother.

Sometimes the two codes are the same. Sometimes one code dominates the other code and hides it in the child. The characteristic we see in the child is the leader or dominant code. Sometimes the codes from both parents mix and both codes show up in the child's characteristic.

In the early 20th century, Reginald Punnett created a system called the "Punnett Square" to help scientists. We still use this simple method today to calculate the likelihood a characteristic has of being passed to the next generation. Young gardeners can use the Punnett Square method to figure the possibilities of a brother or sister having blue eyes or brown eyes. It can even be used to figure the possibilities of plant characteristics.

Let young gardeners be scientists. Pass out The Possibilities activity (Appendix B, page 150). Tell them that both of the parents in this activity have brown eyes. Explain that both were born with two codes for their eye color, one blue and one brown. The BROWN code hides the blue color. This exercise can be modified to use pets instead of siblings. It is up to the instructor to make the needed substitutions.

When the parents have a child, that child might have only brown codes or only blue codes or both codes. Each box in the square represents the possibilities or groups of codes the child has of getting a BROWN code or a blue code from this mom and dad. Explain that if the box has even one BROWN code, the child's eyes will be brown. The only way a child will have blue eyes is if both codes that were passed to that child are blue. Have gardeners color in the eyes using the given codes above and beside the boxes.

Use the following guidelines to help lead a group discussion.

Discussion Questions

1. How many different combinations of colors are possible? (four)
2. How likely is it that a brother or sister will get the BROWN, BROWN codes? (one)
3. How likely is it that a brother or sister will get a BROWN code and a blue code? (two)
4. How likely is it that a brother or sister will get the blue, blue codes? (one)
5. What color of eyes will this brother or sister most likely have? (brown)

Explain that, much in the same way scientists determine possible characteristics in people, the possibility of characteristics can also be determined in plants. If a scientist needs to grow larger fruit, such as a larger tomato, the scientist might take the seeds from two tomatoes that happened to grow extra large and make those plants the parent plants for other tomatoes. The tomatoes that came from the extra large parents most likely will be larger. Other characteristics scientists might work to develop are stronger cotton fibers to make clothes last longer or even a maroon carrot that is more healthful because it contains higher amounts of vitamins, minerals or phytochemicals.

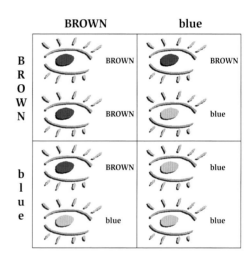

In the Classroom

Bring in a math component and use the Punnett Square to determine fractions or percentages.

Example: If each box equals one possibility then the possibilities are: ¼ BROWN, BROWN; ½ BROWN, blue; ¼ blue, blue.

Have learners calculate the different boxes into fractions: ¼, ½, ³/₄ or 1.

Challenge the class to take the fractions and determine the number of children that would likely have blue eyes in a family of four children or eight children.

All People Are Special

Objective: To learn more about careers in nutrition and health
Time: 45 minutes
Materials: All People are Special (Appendix B, page 151), pencils

Everyone is special and, sometimes, special people have special eating needs. Invite a visitor or take a trip to a local hospital, extended care facility or nursing home and visit with a dietitian who helps people with their special eating needs. Have the group members prepare to interview the professional. They can use questions from the All People are Special page to record the information, or conduct an interview with the nutrition expert in front of an audience.

After the visit, let gardeners discuss what they have learned. Ask them to keep this page in their Garden Journal. Remind gardeners that each and every one of us is special.

QUESTIONS FROM THE INTERVIEW PAGE

1. What is a dietitian?

2. Did you go to college?

3. What subjects do you use in your job? (Math, science, reading)

4. Do special people go to you or do you visit them at their home?

5. Do you help kids?

6. Do you help moms and dads?

7. Do you help grandparents?

8. What kind of special people do you help the most?

9. Which foods should our group eat the most?

10. What is your most favorite thing about your job?

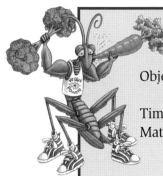

When I Grow Up

Objective: To learn about the choices one needs to make when choosing a career and to identify career options

Time: 30 to 40 minutes

Materials: 9-inch by 12-inch construction paper (one sheet per gardener), scissors, glue or paste, magazines or catalogs, markers, crayons or pencils Before this activity: Write a letter of the alphabet at the top of each sheet of construction paper.

Encourage the gardeners to name the different types of jobs adults have. List these on a piece of paper or the chalkboard. Let them share what kinds of work their parents do and what they'd like to do when they grow up. Give each gardener a sheet of construction paper, and have each cut out magazine photos or draw pictures of the various jobs that begin with that letter of the alphabet. The children also can list people they know or famous people who work in that career. Once completed, compile all the individual letters into a group Career Book.

EXAMPLE:

Aa   astronaut, actor
Bb   baker, banker, businessman
Cc   cowgirl, crane operator
Dd   doctor, dietitian
Ee   economist, engineer, electrician
Ff   food scientist, farmer, father
Gf   gardener, grocer
Hh   helicopter pilot, hairdresser
Ii   ice cream vendor
Jj   janitor, jockey, judge
Kk   king, karate instructor
Ll   lifeguard, lawyer
Mm   mail carrier, mother
Nn   nurse
Oo   operator, optician, occupational therapist
Pp   pilot, producer, plant breeder, physical therapist
Qq   queen, quarterback
Rr   repairman, race car driver
Ss   singer, secretary, soldier
Tt   typist, teacher, trainer
Uu   usher, undertaker
Vv   violinist, veterinarian
Ww   word processor, waitress
Xx   X-ray technician
Yy   youth minister, yoga instructor
Zz   zookeeper

Service Learning and Leadership Development Projects

Feast of Plenty — Host a harvest feast; invite family, friends, etc., to share in the garden surplus. Provide demonstrations and tours of the gardens, displays and rewards.

Pass-along Patch — Develop and establish a berry patch for future groups. The first group establishes the patch and passes it to a second group. The second group adopts it and passes the patch to a third group, and so on. Most berry patches will produce within the first few years, depending on the variety.

Making Cents — Demonstrate ways to conserve resources through gardening. Group members are able to experience first hand money-saving techniques that they can pass along to other groups or to the community.

Create your Own — Create your own community service project.

Appendix A:

Garden Preparation
and Planting Instructions

Getting Started

This section discusses the basic steps in establishing a garden, as well as more specific tips on gardening with children through JMG youth gardening projects. This information can be used as a handy reference guide with any of the JMG garden projects or units. Keep it handy as you plan your program!

Each garden step is followed by a brief discussion of the topic and list of activities relating to the topic which your JMG group can do. As the leader, you will need some background information and a general plan before beginning. However, we encourage you to involve your group as much as possible in the garden development process. Let group members participate in selecting the site and deciding what to grow. You will be empowering them to develop leadership and teamwork skills, which are an essential part of the JMG Golden Ray Series program.

Garden Planning and Preparation

Site Selection: What location will be best?
Take some time to think through the following factors before deciding on a location for your garden. You may save yourself a lot of inconvenience and frustration later!

The site should have:

• **easy access.** Locate it as close as possible to the building where your group meets. The easier it is to access, the more convenient it is for you and your group members to use, and the more use you will get out of it. A close location also usually results in better maintenance and a lower potential for vandalism, and makes those inevitable trips back inside for forgotten supplies or for bathroom breaks easier to manage.

• **a sunny location.** Gardens, especially vegetable gardens, need at least 6 to 8 hours of full sun each day. If you only have access to a shady location, you can plan a specialty shade garden, but you won't be able to grow many vegetables. A shady spot near the garden is great for rest breaks, and if your garden has partial shade from trees or nearby buildings for part of the day, that is fine.

• **a nearby water source.** This is critical. You will need access to water for watering the garden as well as for tool (and child) cleanup. Lugging water hoses across a field is inconvenient and difficult, and can result in very low water pressure. If access to the water faucet is restricted and a key is required, make friends with the maintenance person in charge early in the process!

• **loose, well-drained soil.** Locate the garden in a spot where water drains well after rain. Constantly wet or waterlogged soil will drown plant roots. Well tilled, raised beds enclosed by landscape timbers, or other edging will greatly improve water drainage and air movement in soil.

• **space nearby for tool and equipment storage.** You will need to have access to a storage closet, corner of a classroom, or shed for storing the tools, water hoses, seed trays, bags of potting soil or mulch, and the many other items that accumulate with any garden. The closer this space is to the garden the better. You don't want to have to coordinate a major transport effort each time your group goes to the garden.

In general, think through the potential site from all possible angles. Make it as easy and convenient as possible on both yourself and your JMG group. You want your group to spend time learning about and enjoying the garden not wasting time carrying supplies or enjoying the experience less because it is inconvenient or difficult to manage.

Planting Guidelines

There are two basic methods of planting: direct seeding and transplanting. Most gardens use a combination of both methods. In addition to the suggestions below, refer to the planting guide and chart Appendix B, page 127-130.

Direct seeding

- Direct seeding is simply planting seeds directly into the garden. Many of the most commonly grown vegetables and flowers are planted this way.

- Direct seeding offers several advantages over transplanting. A packet of seeds is usually cheaper than a pack of transplants, you get many more seeds, and you have a much broader selection of plant varieties to choose from. For example, you can select from hundreds of specialty varieties of lettuce to find cultivars especially suited for your region, or bred for specific characteristics with regard to disease resistance, taste or color. If you buy transplants from the nursery, however, you may have only a few varieties to select from.

- Some plants, especially root crops like carrots and radishes, have to be planted from seed because transplanting disturbs their roots and may stunt their growth. They are best planted where they are to grow. For this reason, it is rare that you will find them as transplants.

- Seeds can be purchased from your local nursery or garden center, or can be ordered from seed company catalogs. Looking through seed catalogs and making a wish list is a fun project for adults and kids alike and will give your group practice in garden planning and design.

- Seed companies may offer catalogs free of charge and many will usually send you multiple copies for your group to use in garden planning projects. If you let them know you are working with a JMG youth gardening program, many companies will donate seeds or allow you to purchase at a discount. Plant people are great!

- Follow planting directions on the seed packet carefully! The most common mistakes when planting seeds are planting them too deep or washing them away when watering. When planting seeds, a general rule of thumb is to plant them two to four times as deep as they are wide. However, some seeds have special requirements with regard to planting depth. Check the packet!

- Newly planted seeds must be kept moist until they germinate, form their own root systems and are capable of absorbing water from the soil. Use a very gentle spray to avoid washing seeds out of their rows. Watering wands work great for children and the garden.

Transplanting

- Transplanting is planting small plants (called plantlets, seedlings or transplants) in your garden. They can be multipacks or small pots of plants purchased from a nursery or seedlings that your JMG group raised indoors.

- Some plants take a long time to grow and establish themselves, so they usually are sown indoors and are transplanted out to the garden as growing plants at the appropriate time. Examples are tomatoes and peppers.

- Still other plants are difficult to grow from seed and may require special conditions or long periods of time to germinate. These include some herbs like rosemary and lavender. They are best purchased from the nursery as transplants.
- Transplanting is more expensive per plant than direct seeding, but most crops grown from transplants require less time, space and seed. For example, one four-pack of tomato transplants will produce many tomatoes, enough to feed a family of four. Four carrot seeds, on the other hand, will only produce four or fewer carrots.
- Starting seeds indoors is an excellent project. The main ingredient needed for most healthy seedlings is a lot of light bright indirect light from a window or artificial light. Without adequate light, seedlings will be spindly and unhealthy and will not perform well in the garden.

Garden Maintenance

- **Thinning** is very important. If all of the planted seeds sprout, there will be too many seedlings clustered together for all of them to grow and develop properly. Some seedlings must be removed so the remaining ones have the space they need. It can be difficult to pull up seedlings that you have nurtured, but it is important. Follow the directions on the seed packet regarding spacing requirements for different plants.
- **Fertilizing** should be included in the garden maintenance plan. In order to be healthy and produce a good harvest, garden plants need supplemental fertilizer. Many different fertilizers are available. Most are either granular or liquid. Granular fertilizers can be incorporated into the planting rows or holes at the time of planting. Halfway through the growing season, a second application will be needed. This can be done by "side dressing"– spreading a small line of fertilizer along the side of a row or mound of plants approximately 8 inches from the crown and covering the fertilizer with topsoil. This gets the fertilizer within reach of the plants' roots. Liquid fertilizers are added to water and sprayed onto plants. Some of the fertilizer is absorbed into the soil and taken into plants through the roots. However, liquid feed fertilizers also can be absorbed directly into plants through their leaves.

Make sure to read the fertilizer label carefully so that you know what you are getting, and apply the correct amount according to directions. More fertilizer does not equal more plant growth. If plants get too much fertilizer, or if concentrated fertilizer is left on plant leaves, the plants may experience fertilizer burn and die. Fertilizer burn is evidenced by burning of leaf tips and dead, shriveled bottom leaves at the base of the plant.

- **Stakes** will have to be added for plants that vine or are top heavy, such as cucumbers, pole beans, gourds and tomatoes. You can use purchased tomato cages or make your own, make a tepee out of bamboo, broom or mop handles, or make a wooden A-frame with a string latticework for plants to grow on. Get creative – staking can be a fun group project to do after the busy planting phase is completed. The Bean Tepee activity can be used to grow many vine crops.

- **Weeding** needs to be done at least weekly so weeds don't build up around plants or the garden area. A weed is any unwanted plant. One large, established weed is much harder to pull than many small weeds. The good thing about weeding is that it goes quickly when done regularly and it enhances the close observation skills of your gardeners. Make weeding a part of your weekly routine and let your gardeners write their observations in journals.

- **Pest inspection** will need to be done periodically. If you have a garden with many different varieties of plants, you will probably not have too many pest outbreaks. When multiple smaller crops are produced, large numbers of pests do not usually build up as they do when one crop is grown in a large area (a monoculture). Monocultures allow large numbers of pest populations to build up, resulting in the need for more frequent spraying. Maintaining healthy plants also will lessen pest damage; weak, malnourished or weed-ridden plants are prone to attract pests. Still, the most diversified, well-maintained garden will have an occasional pest outbreak. Develop a plan in advance so you can act quickly to minimize damage. The Texas AgriLife Extension Service recommends IPM (Integrated Pest Management) as a pest management strategy. *Refer to* Who Goes There? (page 14)

Check with your officials to find out what other regulations there are and follow them! There may be a designated person for pesticide applications or restrictions as to when they can be applied. Also, rules for schools or private businesses may be different than those for homeowners.

- **Watering**

  - Newly seeded or planted areas need to be checked daily and kept moist until the plantlets/seedlings establish root systems and are able to absorb moisture from surrounding soil. Seedlings get their water from the immediate root zone area.

  - Once plants are established, usually after 1 to 2 weeks, they will need longer but less frequent watering. It is better to water two to three times a week than to sprinkle lightly everyday. Deeper watering encourages roots to penetrate deeper into the soil. Surface watering results in shallow roots that dry out quickly and makes the plants more susceptible to drought and disease conditions.

  - All plants do not use water at the same rate. Some are more drought tolerant than others. Show your gardeners how to check whether their plants need water. If you stick your finger into the top inch of the soil (about to the first knuckle) and it is dry, then water. If the soil is damp under the surface, it doesn't need water. Signs of wilting may mean plants need water. Wilting can also be a sign of over watering, so make sure you check soil moisture with your finger.

  - Watch out for the water hose! Strong blasts of water can uproot and wash away plants. Make watering cans out of plastic 1-gallon milk jugs with holes punched in the lids. This allows each gardener to have a controlled amount of water to irrigate the garden. The jugs can be refilled easily if more water is needed. Each child gets to water his/her own plants. The garden is not a sodden mess!

• **Tools and Equipment**
There is no set list of required tools and equipment for children's gardens. Review these suggestions and develop a list that will best fit your needs.

- Tools can be borrowed for volunteer work days when you will have more adults at work. However, one or two shovels, rakes and hoes are good to have on hand for ongoing maintenance needs.

- Inexpensive child-sized shovels, rakes and hoes can be found at many hardware stores or garden centers. These are great for kids because they are not play tools. They have wooden handles and metal heads, just like standard-sized tools, but are proportioned smaller for children. You can also adapt standard-sized tools by cutting off handles.

- Garden bed preparation, especially with raised beds, will require shovels and rakes for mixing and spreading soil. However, once the garden is established, children can do almost everything they will need to do with hand tools. These are less expensive to purchase and replace if lost or broken, and present less safety hazards for use with groups of children.

- Make sure to go over safety rules with your group. Claw-type tools should be avoided with younger gardeners.

- Remember to include in your list (and budget) items such as soil, mulch, compost or manure (if it will need to be purchased), a wheelbarrow or cart, watering hoses, and seed trays or pots. These may not be tools, but they will definitely be needed and will add to your costs.

- Before buying any tools or supplies, make a list of what is needed. Review the list to determine which items will be donated and which can be purchased with coupons or food stamps.

Garden Management Tips for Group Leaders

Managing Students

While big groups can work larger areas of garden space, smaller groups of five or fewer students are more successful and easier to manage. Small groups allow for more ownership of garden plots, and provide opportunities for exploration and observation, as well as for individual responsibilities within projects.

Gardeners are naturally active, so plan for them to stay busy in the garden. Gardeners who sit waiting for their turn to work in the garden likely will be distracted and bored. Either pull groups of students away from a larger group activity to work in the garden or give each of the groups specific tasks to complete.

While one small group is weeding, another group could be measuring growth and another watering the plants of their individual gardens. Also, it is a good idea to have an assignment to do when the gardening task is completed. This assignment will serve as a time buffer for the group members that finish early or at different times. For example, as group members finish their jobs, they might have the responsibility of writing in the journals, clearing an area of litter, writing thank-you notes to helpers, sketching from the garden, taking leaf rubbings, or relaxing with a book.

Another successful method is to have gardeners rotate through different tasks so that each person can experience all activities.

Getting Help: Recruiting Volunteers

Use volunteers to aid in managing small groups and give gardeners individual attention. Don't be hesitant to ask for volunteer help with garden projects. Schedule work days that include youths as well as parents, grandparents, Master Gardeners, and local professionals. Such days can accomplish a great deal and establish a shared ownership of the garden. Contact your coordinator to ask for and schedule help.

In addition to scheduled workdays, you probably will need to get help from other adults in recruiting donations and other activities. Establish a JMG Garden Committee to keep those involved updated on garden plans and developments, and to help spread out some of the duties involved in coordinating a JMG garden program. Your JMG Committee can include administrative supervisors, such as principals or agency representatives, program coworkers and maintenance staff, such as teachers and custodians, parent volunteers, and of course, student representatives from the JMG group.

Funding Your Garden

Gardening can be done by spending very little money or it can be a large expense, depending on the amount of supplies and type of structure that are used. Some groups start with a small garden and eventually develop landscapes complete with benches, arbors and greenhouses. However, it is more important to use the garden as a learning environment than to fund an elaborate setup. Decide with your group what type of garden you want to develop, what it will cost and what supplies you will need, and create a master plan for implementation. It is a good idea to start off small. Garden establishment and startup efforts require a great deal of time, and you want the project to be enjoyable and successful rather than a cumbersome task.

There are many ways to obtain the supplies and funds that you will need for your garden. Following are a few suggestions, but they are by no means the only options. Be creative!

- **Donations** of supplies, plants and seeds are often easier to obtain than money with which to buy them. Local nurseries will often donate plants and/or seeds. Local landscapers may donate topsoil, mulch or landscape plants for the garden, especially if they have children in your school or program. A wish list sent home with students can often generate donations of equipment such as an old wheelbarrow or cart, watering hoses and sprinklers, or pots and buckets to use as planting containers. Remember to thank donors; have gardeners write thank-you letters or put a sign thanking sponsors in the garden. This provides them with free advertising, and can help generate future donations.

- ***Fundraisers*** planned and coordinated by gardeners generate funds to purchase garden tools and other needed items, and also enable gardeners to develop business and leadership skills. Baked goods or other products can be sold to generate initial funds. After the garden is established, there are many garden products, like fresh produce and herbal crafts, that can be sold. Many school garden programs establish accounts and use funds from sales to pay for tools and equipment or to generate scholarships for students. You can do the same with your JMG group.
- ***Grants*** are available to fund hands-on education programs such as JMG youth gardens. There is a vast array of grants for which you can apply. These include local community block grants, private foundation grants and state and federally funded grant programs. Be aware, though, that grant writing is a long process and can take a great deal of time. Most grants require extensive documentation of program plans and goals, and can take 6 months to a year or more before approval or rejection. Local programs usually offer the best chance for success on an individual garden level. Check with your local garden clubs, garden centers, and community service agencies for potential programs.
- It is critical to **generate publicity** through the local newspaper and *make contacts* with local and regional community leaders to promote awareness of your program and its benefits for local youths, and to create an awareness of your needs. Local support, volunteer assistance and donations of equipment and funds often result from such community awareness.

Safety Considerations

Always remember to consider safety issues first in any project. Tool safety should be reviewed with gardeners. Also, know in advance of any allergies that your gardeners may have. Work with a school nurse and/or parents to develop a proactive safety plan in case of stings, bites, or exposures to plant allergies.

Vandalism

Vandalism is an unfortunate possibility that comes along with gardening in public spaces. In community gardens, the vandals may be older children from the area or teenagers roaming the neighborhood after hours. Leaders who have gone through vandalism experiences with their students tend to regard it as an unfortunate fact of life that brings home some powerful lessons for young gardeners. Their advice: If it happens, make it a part of the learning experience. Explain to gardeners that vandalism is a hurtful act and use the experience to initiate discussion on social responsibility, respect for self and others, and personal choices when dealing with peer pressure. *Don't use vandalism as a reason to not garden.*

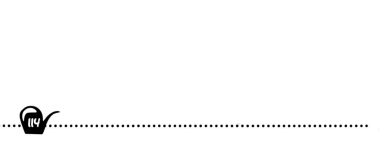

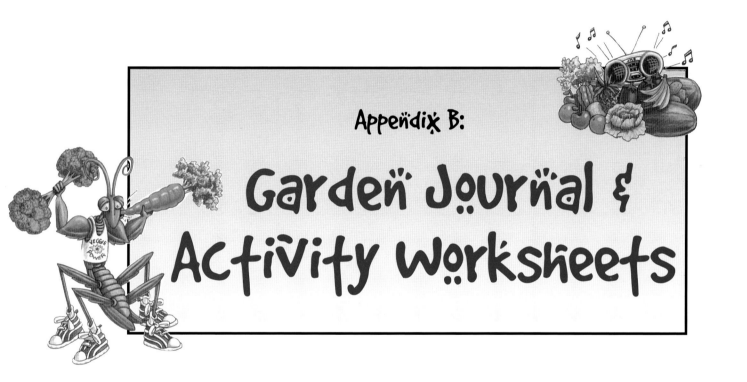

Appendix B:

Garden Journal & Activity Worksheets

Name:_____

Garden Journal Page

USE THIS PAGE TO WRITE ABOUT YOUR GARDEN.

Ideas to write about: how your garden looks, if the soil is wet or dry, if the plants are having problems, how the plants change, if you find any insects or anything else you want to write about. Make a small sketch to show something you are writing about.

Date	Notes	Sketch

Name:_____

Journal Page

This vegetable is _____

Dates I harvested from this plant:

_____
_____
_____
_____
_____
_____

Insects and diseases I noticed on this plant that I want to remember:

_____
_____
_____
_____
_____
_____
_____

✂ -

This vegetable is _____

Dates I harvested from this plant:

_____
_____
_____
_____
_____
_____

Insects and diseases I noticed on this plant that I want to remember:

_____
_____
_____
_____
_____
_____
_____

Name: _____

Harvest Time Line

Write the names of the vegetables harvested from the garden under the word "Vegetable." Then create a time line by graphing the months you harvested each vegetable from your garden. Use your journal pages to determine the dates of harvest. Example: If tomatoes were harvested from June through September, a line would appear from June through September.

Vegetable	Jan	Feb	Mar	Apr	May	June	July	Aug	Sept	Oct	Nov	Dec
Example: Tomato							———	———	———			

The vegetable harvested for the longest time was _____.

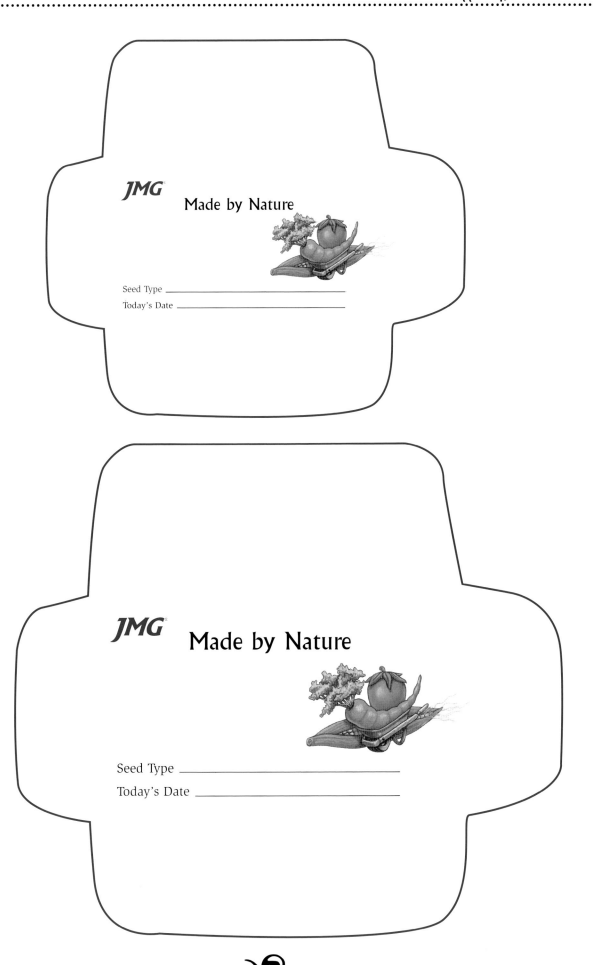

JMG

Made by Nature

Seed Type _____

Today's Date _____

JMG

Made by Nature

Seed Type _____

Today's Date _____

Name: _____

Name: _____

Name: _____

10 in 2

Write in the amount you can spend (your budget) on the first line of each day's menu. Plan a menu for 2 days to include 10 fruits and vegetables (5 servings daily) for your family. Then add up how much money you will need to prepare the meals. Write this total on the line labeled "Meals for the day will cost." Subtract the second amount from the first amount and put the difference in the "Money saved" line.

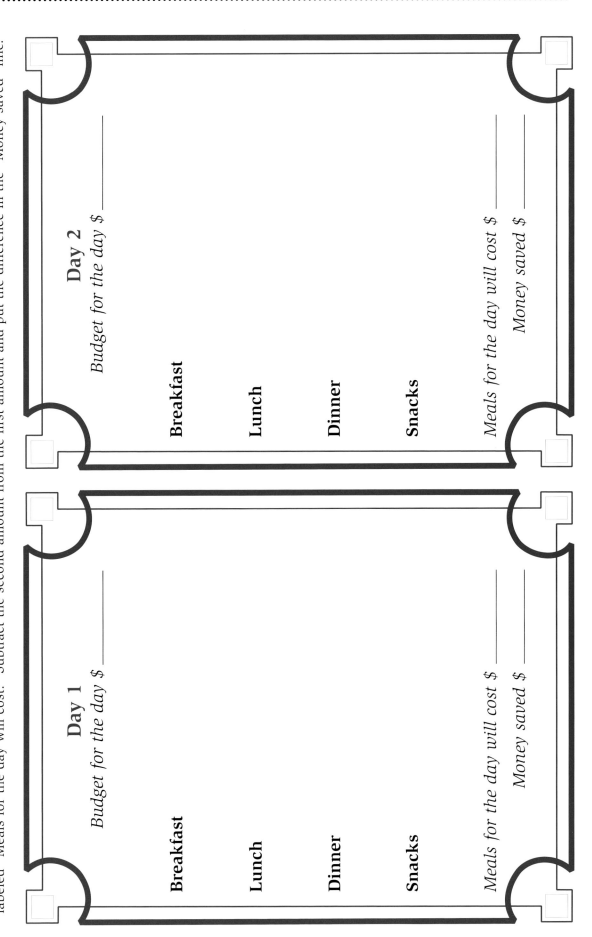

Day 1

Budget for the day $ _____

Breakfast

Lunch

Dinner

Snacks

Meals for the day will cost $ _____

Money saved $ _____

Day 2

Budget for the day $ _____

Breakfast

Lunch

Dinner

Snacks

Meals for the day will cost $ _____

Money saved $ _____

Name:_____

P.L.A.N.T. Needs

What do plants need?

P _____

L _____

A _____

N _____

T _____

S _____

Name: _____

Site Selection Survey

You are trying to decide on the best place to put your group's garden. Circle one number for each line. A "1" means it's not very good and a "5" is the best.

LOCATION OF SITE:

Area has sunlight	1	2	3	4	5
Area is near a water source	1	2	3	4	5
Area has good soil	1	2	3	4	5
Area is near where tools are stored	1	2	3	4	5
Area is close by and easy to get to	1	2	3	4	5

Add up all of the numbers in the box above and write it in the star.

What is this site's score?

LOCATION OF SITE:

Area has sunlight	1	2	3	4	5
Area is near a water source	1	2	3	4	5
Area has good soil	1	2	3	4	5
Area is near where tools are stored	1	2	3	4	5
Area is close by and easy to get to	1	2	3	4	5

Add up all of the numbers in the box above and write it in the star.

What is this site's score?

LOCATION OF SITE:

Area has sunlight	1	2	3	4	5
Area is near a water source	1	2	3	4	5
Area has good soil	1	2	3	4	5
Area is near where tools are stored	1	2	3	4	5
Area is close by and easy to get to	1	2	3	4	5

Add up all of the numbers in the box above and write it in the star.

What is this site's score?

Which site has the highest score? _____

Where did you choose to put your garden? Why did you choose this place?

Name:_____

Who Goes There?

draw me here

AM I BENEFICIAL?

Leave me alone and let
me work for you

AM I A PEST?

ARE THERE JUST A FEW OF US

ON YOUR PLANT?

Pick us off with your hands
and squash us!

ARE THERE LOTS OF US ON

YOUR PLANT?

Spray with water to knock
us off your plant.

DID THIS WORK?

YES

Congratulations, you did it!

NO

Can the plant be removed?

YES

Remove the plant and con-
tinue watering other plants
for pests.

NO

Try a beneficial insect. You
can buy them at your local
nursery.

If it doesn't control the
pest, ask an adult to apply
an appropriate pesticide.

Name:_____

Who Goes There?

Write about the insects you find in the garden and draw what they look like.

_____

_____

_____

_____

_____

_____

_____

_____

Name:_____

Paper Pot Transplants

Draw a picture of what your plant looks like when you pull it out of the container. Look closely at the roots and draw them, too.

Name:_____

Fall Planting Guide

The time to plant vegetables is based on the weather. Plant crops that will be harmed by cold weather early enough in the fall so that they mature before the first freeze.* Cold-hardy crops can withstand all but the coldest of weather and are usually planted later.

If a frost occurs earlier than usual, some plants may be damaged and some of the harvest may be lost. To protect plants from frost, cover them with a light blanket, a clear plastic shower curtain or a row cover.

Some crops listed in the chart have special needs that are explained below.

♣ Garlic is grown by dividing a head into individual cloves and planting each clove. Onions can be grown from seed; however, they usually are planted as "sets" or small onions in late fall to early winter. Potatoes are grown by planting "seed" potatoes, which are sections of large potatoes that have been cut into chunks that include at least one "eye," or node. The new growth comes from these nodes.

T Transplants can be grown either by seed or by purchasing a transplant–you can do both. Tomatoes are not included in the seed list. They should be grown from transplants in the fall or started from seed in midsummer. Plant the transplants so that the root ball is completely covered with a soil later no more than 1/4-inch thick. If the root ball is left exposed, the plant may dry out and die. Burying the root ball too deep can result in plant rot from a buried stem.

The recommended planting dates can vary greatly depending on where you live. Contact your county Extension office for information to complete your Fall Planting Chart.

Name:_____

fall Planting chart

Crop	Recommended planting date	Number of seeds per paper towel	Planting depth	Days to harvest	Country of origin
Root Crops					
Beets		9	1/2"	55-70	Mediterranean area
Carrots		16	1/4"	70-80	Afghanistan
Garlic ♣		16	1"	100-200	Pakistan
Onions ♣		16	1"	80-120	Pakistan
Potatoes ♣		1	4"	70-90	Chile and Peru
Radishes		16	1/2"	25-40	China and Middle Asia
Turnips		9	1/2"	30-60	Mediterranean area
Leaf Crops					
Brussels sprouts		1	1/4" or T	120-150	Mediterranean area
Cabbage		1	1/4" or T	60-120	Mediterranean area
Chard		4	1"	45-80	Mediterranean area
Collards		4	1/2"	45-80	Mediterranean area
Kohlrabi		1	1/2"	50-75	Mediterranean area
Lettuce (leaf)		4	1/4" or T	45-60	Egypt or Iran
Lettuce (head)		4	1/2" or T	45-90	Egypt or Iran
Mustard greens		4	1/2"	30-50	Mediterranean area
Spinach		9	1/2"	40-60	Iran
Turnip greens		4	1/2"	30-60	Mediterranean area
Flower/Fruit Crops					
Beans (bush)		4	1"	45-60	Mexico & SW U.S.
Beans (pole)		4	2"	50-70	Mexico & SW U.S.
Broccoli		1	1/4" or T	60-80	Mediterranean area
Cauliflower		1	1/4" or T	60-100	Mediterranean area
Cucumbers		2	1"	50-70	India
Squash		1 seed per 4 squares	1"	45-90	Mexico & SW U.S.
Tomatoes		1	1/4" or T	60-80	Andes Mountains in South America

Name:_____

Spring Planting Guide

The time to plant vegetables is based on weather. In the spring, plant vegetables that can be injured by cold after all danger of frosty weather is past.* Plant cold-hardy vegetables before this frost-free date, which is usually early enough for them to mature before the weather gets too hot.

Remember that the last frost date is an average. If a frost occurs later than average, it may damage some plants and some of the harvest may be lost. Protect your plants from a late frost by covering them with a light blanket, a clear plastic shower curtain or a row cover.

Some crops listed in the chart have special needs that are explained below.

♣ Potatoes are grown by planting "seed" potatoes, which are sections of large potatoes that have been cut into chunks that include at least one "eye" or node. The new growth comes from these nodes. Shallots can be grown from seeds; however, they usually are planted as "sets" or small bulbs in early winter.

♠ Vine crops are grown on raised beds with 7 to 10 feet between each row. You can plant squash, cucumber and small watermelon varieties closer together; dwarf varieties need the least amount of space between plants. You can conserve space between rows by using a trellis that allows vines and fruits to grow vertically. This method may also discourage disease.

T Transplants can be grown either by seed or by purchasing a transplant–you can do both. Tomatoes are not included in the seed list. They should be grown from transplants in the fall or started from seed in midsummer. Plant the transplants so that the root ball is completely covered with a soil later no more than 1/4-inch thick. If the root ball is left exposed, the plant may dry out and die. Burying the root ball too deep can result in plant rot from a buried stem.

The recommended planting dates can vary greatly depending on where you live. Contact your county Extension office for information to complete your Spring Planting Chart.

Name:_____

Spring Planting chart

Crop	First planting dates	Number of seeds per paper towel	Planting depth	Days to harvest	Country of origin
Root Crops					
Potatoes ♣ (Irish)		1	4" - 6"	70-90	Chile and Peru
Carrots		16	1/4"	70-80	Chile and Peru
Shallots		4	1"	80-120	Asia
Radishes		16	1/2"	28-40	Chile and Peru
Leaf Crops					
Cabbage, Chinese		1	1/2"	65-70	Asia
Lettuce, Leaf		4	1/4" or T	45-60	Egypt or Iran
Mustard Greens		4	1/4" or T	30-50	Mediterranean area
Parsley		4	T	20-120	Mediterranean area
Spinach		9	1/2"	40-60	Iran
Turnip Greens		4	1/2"	30-60	Mediterranean area
Flower/Fruit Crops					
Eggplant		1 plant per 1 square	T	80-90	Asia
Muskmelon ♠ (Cantaloupe)		1 seed per 4 squares	1/2" - 1"	90-120	Asia and Africa
Cucumbers ♠		1	1/2" - 1"	50-70	Asia
Peppers ♣		1 plant per 2 squares	T	80-100	South America
Squash (Summer)		1 seed per 4 squares	1"	50-60	North America
Tomato		1 seed per 4 squares	T	30	Andes Mountains in South America
Watermelon ♠		1 seed per 9 squares	1" - 2"	80-100	Africa
Seed Crops					
Beans, Lima (bush)		2	1"	64-80	Mexico & Central America
Beans, Lima (pole)		4	1"	75-85	Mexico & Central America
Beans, Snap (bush)		4	1"	45-60	Central America
Beans, Snap (pole)		2	1"	60-70	Central America
Corn, Sweet		1	2"	70-90	South America
Peas, English		12	1" - 2"	55-90	Europe and Asia
Peas, Black-eyed		2	1" - 2"	60-70	Asia

Name:_____

Make Your Pick

WHICH PLANT DID YOU CHOOSE?

WHY DID YOU CHOOSE THAT PLANT?

DRAW A PICTURE OF WHAT YOU THINK YOUR PLANT WILL LOOK LIKE WHEN IT IS MATURE.

_____

_____

_____

_____

Name:_____

JMG Veggie Research

Name of plant:_____

DRAWING OF PLANT:

DRAWING OF SEEDS:

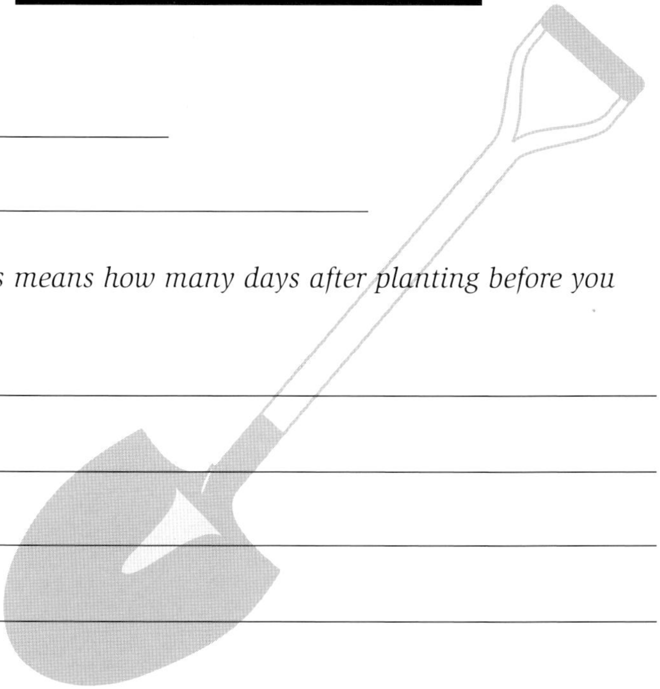

Season plant is grown:_____

How deep should the seed be planted?_____

How many days until plant can be harvested? *(This means how many days after planting before you can pick a vegetable that has grown on the plant.)*

How do you eat it? (fresh, fried, boiled, steamed)_____

What continent did it come from?_____

What vitamins does this vegetable have in it?_____

Why did you choose to plant this vegetable?_____

_____

Write two interesting facts that you learned about this plant.

1._____

_____

2._____

_____

Name:_____

Parts of the Potato

OBSERVATIONS: CIRCLE THE WORDS THAT DESCRIBE WHAT YOU SEE IN THE POTATO.

Brown skin
Red skin
Dirt
Scratches
Knots

Write other words that describe the potato here.

FIND AND LABEL THE FOLLOWING PARTS OF THE POTATO:

Tuber   Stems   Node   Leaves

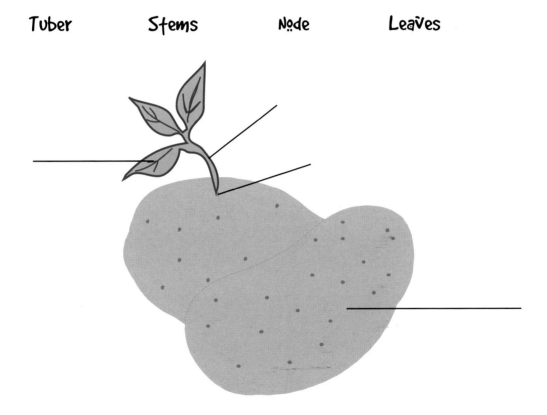

CIRCLE THE CORRECT ANSWER FROM THE CHOICES SHOWN IN PARENTHESES.

1. Potatoes grow (above/below) ground in (hot/warm/cool/cold) temperatures.

2. Potatoes have dimples called (tubers/nodes).

3. Potatoes are not really root crops', they are (special stems/special roots) called (tubers/nodes).

4. Potatoes are good for me because they are full of (sugar/carbohydrates) and Vitamin (A/C).

Name:_____

Pole Race

Which pole bean do you think will be the first to grow to be 5 feet long?

_____

DIRECTIONS: MEASURE THE GROWTH OF EACH VINE ONCE A WEEK OR TWICE A WEEK TO SEE WHICH PLANT GROWS TO BE 5 FEET LONG FIRST.

Date													
Pole 1													
Pole 2													
Pole 3													
Pole 4													
Pole 5													
Pole 6													

GRAPH BELOW THE LENGTH OF THE POLE BEAN VINE THAT YOU CHOSE TO REACH 5 FEET FIRST.

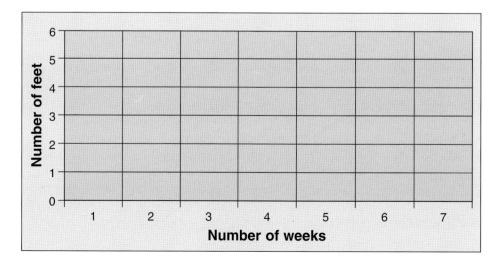

Name:_____

Bold Molds Lab Sheet

Draw a circle around the parts of the experiment below that are the same.

Sunny spot   Vegetable
Fruit
Refrigerator   Dark, dry cabinet

Draw a box around the parts of the experiment above that are the same.

QUESTION

Do you think that at the different temperatures the fruits will have the same amount of mold?

_____

HYPOTHESIS

In the boxes below, draw what you think the fruits will look like after being exposed to the different temperatures for 2 weeks.

EXPERIMENT

List the three locations of your fruit.

_____   _____   _____

RESULTS

Finish this section in 2 weeks!
Did different amounts of mold grow at different temperatures?_____

Draw in the boxes what each fruit actually looks like.

Name:_____

MyPyramid For Kids

Name:_____

Making the Menu

It is important to eat a variety of healthful foods every day. Eating a variety of foods helps you make your meals more nutritious. *For example, applesauce is healthy food choice, but instead of eating applesauce for each meal, it would be more nutritious to have a variety of fruits. This might include applesauce with breakfast, an orange with lunch, grapes with dinner and a banana for snack!*

1. With a couple of friends, look at each meal on the menu below and think about a way to make it more nutritious. Mark out any item you would take off the menu, and write in foods in the next box that would make the meal more nutritious. Make sure that the amounts you write for the meal would be how much you would really eat for that meal.

If you had...	How could you make it more nutritious?

BREAKFAST
    2 doughnuts
    Soda
 	
LUNCH
    Ham sandwich with white bread
    Potato chips
    Apple
    Orange juice
 	
DINNER
    Baked chicken breast
    ¾ cup of white rice
    Lettuce salad with ranch dressing
    Orange juice
 	
SNACKS
    1 cup yogurt
    1 candy bar
    Soda
    4 graham crackers	

2. Now that you've made your meals more nutritious, look at how many different types of fruits you have included in your menu above. Count the total of different fruits and write that number in the fruit box below.

3. Next, do the same for each of the other food groups below:

Menu Variety Count				
Grains	Vegetables	Fruits	Milk	Meats & Beans

4. Do you think your menu for the day includes a good variety of healthy foods?_____

5. Which food group included the greatest variety?_____

6. Which food group could have included more variety?_____

Go to www.mypyramid.gov to find the recommended amounts that your body needs from each food group.

Name: _____

School Menu

BREAKFAST:

LUNCH:

SNACK:

Name:_____

Food Labeling

Directions: Choose four canned or packaged fruits or vegetables found in your home. For each item, use the label on the container to determine percent of the daily value or %DV of calcium, iron, vitamin A, vitamin C and fiber found in one serving. Complete the following, the answer the questions below.

		% Daily Value for
Type of Fruit _____		**Selected Nutrients**
Serving size _____	Vitamin A	_____
Calories _____	Vitamin C	_____
Protein _____	Calcium	_____
Fat _____	Iron	_____
Dietary Fiber _____		_____

		% Daily Value for
Type of Fruit _____		**Selected Nutrients**
Serving size _____	Vitamin A	_____
Calories _____	Vitamin C	_____
Protein _____	Calcium	_____
Fat _____	Iron	_____
Dietary Fiber _____		_____

		% Daily Value for
Type of Fruit _____		**Selected Nutrients**
Serving size _____	Vitamin A	_____
Calories _____	Vitamin C	_____
Protein _____	Calcium	_____
Fat _____	Iron	_____
Dietary Fiber _____		_____

		% Daily Value for
Type of Fruit _____		**Selected Nutrients**
Serving size _____	Vitamin A	_____
Calories _____	Vitamin C	_____
Protein _____	Calcium	_____
Fat _____	Iron	_____
Dietary Fiber _____		_____

1. WHICH FOOD IS HIGHEST IN CALCIUM?_____

2. WHICH FOOD IS HIGHEST IN IRON?_____

3. WHICH FOOD IS HIGHEST IN VITAMIN A?_____

4. WHICH FOOD IS HIGHEST IN VITAMIN C?_____

5. WHICH FOOD IS HIGHEST IN FIBER?_____

6. WHICH FOOD HAS THE MOST SERVINGS?_____

Name:_____

Label Reader

NUTRITION INFORMATION

Serving Size: The amount commonly eaten in one sitting. Be careful: some products contain more than one serving.

Dietary Fiber: Derived from plants and found in foods containing plant parts. Helps the body digest foods and absorb nutrients; helps lower blood cholesterol.

Vitamin A: Helps with night and color vision; helps bones grow and skin develop; helps fight disease.

Vitamin C: Helps fight infections and heals wounds; helps the body absorb iron.

Calcium: Promotes strong bones and teeth; needed for blood to coagulate or thicken; used by muscles and nerves.

Iron: Needed for hemoglobin (the part of the red blood cells that carries oxygen) and myoglobin (the protein in muscle cells that holds oxygen).

Apricots, raw, 3 medium

Calories	50	Total Fat	0
Dietary Fiber	3g	Protein	0
Vitamin A	55%	Vitamin C	18%
Calcium	2%	Iron	3%

Kiwifruit, raw, 1 medium

Calories	46	Total Fat	0
Dietary Fiber	3g	Protein	1g
Vitamin A	3%	Vitamin C	123%
Calcium	2%	Iron	2%

Cantaloupe, pieces, 1 cup

Calories	56	Total Fat	0
Dietary Fiber	1g	Protein	1g
Vitamin A	103%	Vitamin C	113%
Calcium	2%	Iron	2%

Apple, raw, 1 medium with skin

Calories	80	Total Fat	0
Dietary Fiber	4g	Protein	0
Vitamin A	2%	Vitamin C	13%
Calcium	1%	Iron	1%

Grapefruit, raw, 1/2 medium (pink & red)

Calories	40	Total Fat	0
Dietary Fiber	1.4g	Protein	1g
Vitamin A	3%	Vitamin C	70%
Calcium	2%	Iron	0%

Raspberries, raw, 1 cup

Calories	60	Total Fat	1g
Dietary Fiber	8g	Protein	1g
Vitamin A	3%	Vitamin C	50%
Calcium	3%	Iron	4%

Source: Bowes & Church, Food Values of Portions Commonly Used

Name:_____

Taste Test

Fruit	Color	Texture	Taste	Smell	Total
A	1 2 3 4 5	1 2 3 4 5	1 2 3 4 5	1 2 3 4 5	
B	1 2 3 4 5	1 2 3 4 5	1 2 3 4 5	1 2 3 4 5	
C	1 2 3 4 5	1 2 3 4 5	1 2 3 4 5	1 2 3 4 5	
D	1 2 3 4 5	1 2 3 4 5	1 2 3 4 5	1 2 3 4 5	
E	1 2 3 4 5	1 2 3 4 5	1 2 3 4 5	1 2 3 4 5	

WHICH LETTER HAS THE BIGGEST TOTAL? _____

WHAT FRUIT DO YOU THINK IT IS? _____

Name:_____

Vitamin A Helps Me See, Grow and Play!

Look at the list of fruits below. Rank the fruits according to the amount of vitamin A that they contain. 1 = highest, 10 = lowest

FRUIT	SERVING SIZE	AMOUNT OF VITAMIN A FOUND IN THIS FRUIT (INTERNATIONAL UNITS, IU)	RANK
BANANA	1 medium	92	
CANTALOUPE	1 cup of pieces	5,158	
GRAPEFRUIT	1/2 of a medium	153	
KIWI	1 medium	133	
ORANGE	1 medium	240	
PEACH	1 medium	465	
PINEAPPLE	1 cup of pieces	36	
WATERMELON	1 cup of pieces	586	

Name:_____

Vitamin C is Good for Me!

Look at the list of fruits below. Rank the fruits according to the amount of vitamin C that they contain.
1 = highest, 10 = lowest

FRUIT	SERVING SIZE	AMOUNT OF VITAMIN C FOUND IN THIS FRUIT (INTERNATIONAL UNITS, IU)	RANK
BANANA	1 medium	10	
CANTALOUPE	1 cup of pieces	68	
GRAPEFRUIT	1/2 of a medium	42	
KIWI	1 medium	74	
ORANGE	1 medium	75	
PEACH	1 medium	6	
PINEAPPLE	1 cup of pieces	24	
WATERMELON	1 cup of pieces	15	

Name:_____

Rough and Tough Foods

NO FIBER	GOOD SOURCE OF FIBER

☆☆☆☆☆ EXCELLENT FIBER SOURCE ☆☆☆☆☆

UNKNOWN

What am I?

I am a_____ fiber source.

The food with good fiber is _____ .

☆☆☆☆☆☆☆☆☆☆☆☆☆☆☆☆☆☆☆☆☆☆☆☆☆☆
☆   ☆
☆   **The food with highest fiber is** _____ .   ☆
☆☆☆☆☆☆☆☆☆☆☆☆☆☆☆☆☆☆☆☆☆☆☆☆☆☆

Name:_____

How Much Fiber is Right for Me?

Fiber is a nutrient found in plants. Some people call it "roughage." Eating fiber can help decrease your risk of developing heart disease and come cancers. How much fiber do you need? Moms and dads should try to eat at least 25 grams of fiber each day. Students are a little different. Calculate the amount of fiber that is right for you by using the "age + 5" rule — just take your age and add 5. Example: If you are age 8, then add 8 and 5 for a total of 13 grams of fiber you need each day.

My name is _____ and I am _____ years old.

The amount of fiber that I need each day is _____ (your age) + **5** = _____ grams.

CIRCLE FOODS BELOW THAT ADD UP TO THE AMOUNT OF FIBER THAT YOU NEED EACH DAY.

1 medium apple
3.7 grams

1 medium baked potato
4.6 grams

1 cup strawberries
3.4 grams

12 ounces of soda
0 grams

1 medium orange
3 grams

1 medium carrot
2.2 grams

1/2 cup cooked pinto beans
7.4 grams

1/2 cup cooked oatmeal
2 grams

1/2 cup cooked green beans
2 grams

2 slices of whole wheat bread
3.8 grams

Name:_____

U-B the Judge

TASTE

Taste and rank each fruit sample. A "1" means you liked it the least and "5" means you liked it the best.

FRESH	1 2 3 4 5
FROZEN	1 2 3 4 5
CANNED	1 2 3 4 5

PRICE

With an adult's help, write in the price and circle the ounce (oz.) or pound (lb.) of each sample type. Rank them from "1" to "3." The sample that costs the most receives a "1" and the sample with the lowest cost receives a "3." Circle the sample that costs the least amount of money.

FRESH	$_____ for _____ oz./lbs.	Ranked _____
FROZEN	$_____ for _____ oz./lbs.	Ranked _____
CANNED	$_____ for _____ oz./lbs.	Ranked _____

APPEARANCE

Rank each fruit sample based on appearance. A "1" means you liked its looks the least and "5" means you liked its looks the best.

FRESH	1 2 3 4 5
FROZEN	1 2 3 4 5
CANNED	1 2 3 4 5

Total number of points for: FRESH _____   FROZEN _____   CANNED _____

Draw the WINNER

Blue Ribbon Fruits and Vegetables

Write the name of the fruit or vegetable in the "I am a . . ." blank. Then draw the blue ribbon winner of each fruit or vegetable type in "I look like this . . . ." Finally, write a few words on why you picked the blue ribbon fruit or vegetable above all the others.

I AM A	I LOOK LIKE THIS	I WAS CHOSEN BECAUSE
_____		
_____		
_____		
_____		

Name: _____

Name:_____

Tree of Knowledge

My name is _____ . I am _____ years young.

I interviewed my _____ and they are _____ years young.

WHAT TYPES OF PLANTS HAVE YOU USED TO SOOTHE MINOR BURNS? _____

_____

WHICH PLANTS HAVE YOU USED TO HELP HEAL MINOR SCRAPES AND SCRATCHES? _____

_____

WHAT OTHER PLANTS HAVE YOU USED FOR MEDICINAL PURPOSES?

_____

DO YOU KNOW OF ANY OTHER PLANTS THAT PEOPLE HAVE USED FOR MEDICINAL PURPOSES IN THE PAST OR ARE NOW USING? _____

_____

WHERE DID YOU LEARN TO USE PLANTS THIS WAY? _____

_____

HAVE YOU TAUGHT YOUR CHILDREN YOUR KNOWLEDGE OF PLANTS? _____

_____

Name:_____

Junk Food Blues

I had a big hunger, wanted a tasty treat.
   Grabbed some soda and chips—started to eat
I ate the whole bag of chips, drank a can of soda, too.
   Now I ache somethin' awful—I got the low-down junk food blues.

Chorus:
I'm tired, my stomach hurts, my head and body ache.
   I'm eatin' too much junk food, too many fries and sugar flakes.
Now I want some good food—something my body really needs.
   Payin' attention to what I eat—each time before I feed.

Now I forgot my own song, when I fixed today's lunch.
   I packed some nachos, cookies and candy bar that crunched.
Same thing happened when I ate, 'cause healthy food I did not choose.
   I got that achy, tired feelin'—the low-down junk food blues.

Repeat chorus

Gotta big game today, playing the Mighty Bears.
   Eatin' some candy, lots of sugar, my plan to get prepared.
Wanna be fast and win against this other guy named Fred.
   But the candy didn't work, I lost, my face is sweaty and red.

Repeat chorus

The game was over and they had won, they were happy but I felt sick.
   Saw Fred munchin' on some grapes and some orange carrot sticks.
Then I knew it was my fault, I finally got a clue,
   'Cause all the junk that I ate before, gave me the low-down junk food blues.

Name: _____

The Possibilities

MOM AND DAD

The codes for Mom are BROWN and blue. The codes for Dad are also BROWN and blue. The code for BROWN hides the blue color.

(1) Color the eyes of Mom and Dad brown.

CHILD

Each box in the square represent possible groups of codes for the child of this Mom and Dad. Some of the child's chances might be only BROWN codes or only blue codes or both codes. If a box has even one BROWN code, the child's eyes will be brown. The only way a child will have blue eyes is if both of the codes that were passed to that child are for blue eyes.

(2) In each box, color the eyes of the child using one code from Mom and one code from Dad.

(3) Put a box ☐ around the square(s) with BROWN/BROWN or BROWN/blue codes. Put a circle around the square(s) with blue/blue codes and answer the following:

HOW MANY BROWN/BROWN CODES ARE POSSIBLE?   1   2   3   4

HOW MANY BROWN/blue CODES ARE POSSIBLE?   1   2   3   4

HOW MANY blue/blue CODES ARE POSSIBLE?   1   2   3   4

THIS CHILD IS MOST LIKELY TO HAVE BROWN / blue EYES (CIRCLE ONE).

(4) Color the four possible eye color combination of the child using the table to the right.

DAD	MOM	
	BROWN	blue
BROWN		
blue		

Name:_____

All People are Special

1. WHAT IS A DIETICIAN?

    _____

2. DID YOU HAVE TO GO TO COLLEGE?

    _____

3. WHAT SUBJECTS DO YOU HAVE TO USE IN YOUR JOB (MATH, SCIENCE, READING)?

    _____

4. DO SPECIAL PEOPLE GO TO YOU OR DO YOU VISIT THEM AT THEIR HOME?

    _____

5. DO YOU HELP CHILDREN?

    _____

6. DO YOU HELP MOMS AND DADS?

    _____

7. DO YOU HELP GRANDPARENTS?

    _____

8. WHICH KIND OF SPECIAL PEOPLE DO YOU HELP THE MOST?

    _____

9. WHICH FOODS SHOULD OUR GROUP EAT THE MOST?

    _____

10. WHAT IS YOUR MOST FAVORITE THING ABOUT YOUR JOB?

    _____

Appendix C:

Parental Take-home Sheets

MyPyramid

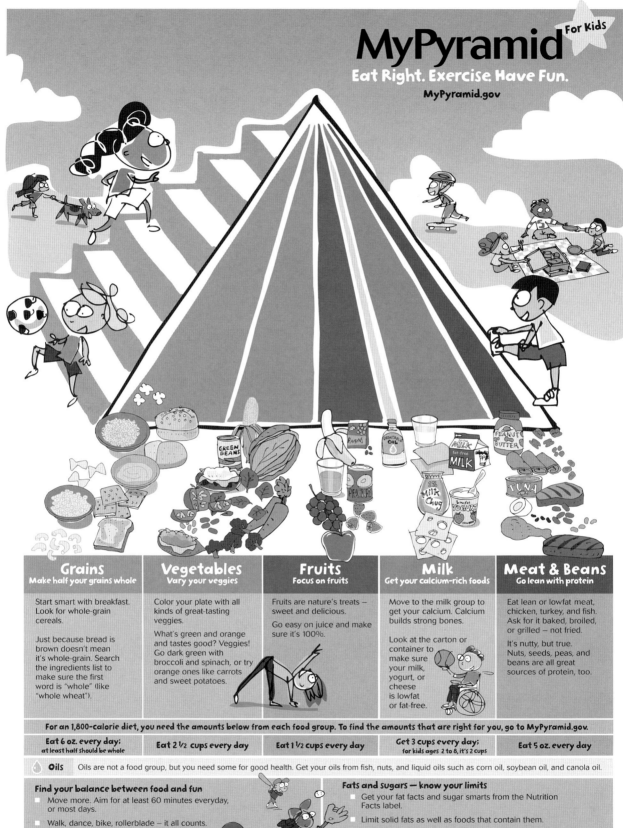

MyPyramid For Kids
Eat Right. Exercise. Have Fun.
MyPyramid.gov

Grains Make half your grains whole	**Vegetables** Vary your veggies	**Fruits** Focus on fruits	**Milk** Get your calcium-rich foods	**Meat & Beans** Go lean with protein
Start smart with breakfast. Look for whole-grain cereals. Just because bread is brown doesn't mean it's whole-grain. Search the ingredients list to make sure the first word is "whole" (like "whole wheat").	Color your plate with all kinds of great-tasting veggies. What's green and orange and tastes good? Veggies! Go dark green with broccoli and spinach, or try orange ones like carrots and sweet potatoes.	Fruits are nature's treats — sweet and delicious. Go easy on juice and make sure it's 100%.	Move to the milk group to get your calcium. Calcium builds strong bones. Look at the carton or container to make sure your milk, yogurt, or cheese is lowfat or fat-free.	Eat lean or lowfat meat, chicken, turkey, and fish. Ask for it baked, broiled, or grilled — not fried. It's nutty, but true. Nuts, seeds, peas, and beans are all great sources of protein, too.

For an 1,800-calorie diet, you need the amounts below from each food group. To find the amounts that are right for you, go to MyPyramid.gov.

Eat 6 oz. every day; at least half should be whole	Eat 2 ½ cups every day	Eat 1 ½ cups every day	Get 3 cups every day; for kids ages 2 to 8, it's 2 cups	Eat 5 oz. every day

Oils Oils are not a food group, but you need some for good health. Get your oils from fish, nuts, and liquid oils such as corn oil, soybean oil, and canola oil.

Find your balance between food and fun
- Move more. Aim for at least 60 minutes everyday, or most days.
- Walk, dance, bike, rollerblade – it all counts. How great is that!

Fats and sugars — know your limits
- Get your fat facts and sugar smarts from the Nutrition Facts label.
- Limit solid fats as well as foods that contain them.
- Choose food and beverages low in added sugars and other caloric sweeteners.

MyPyramid.gov
STEPS TO A HEALTHIER YOU

U.S. Department of Agriculture
Food and Nutrition Service
September 2005
FNS-381

  USDA
teamnutrition.usda.gov

USDA is an equal opportunity provider and employer

Pyramid Eating

MyPyramid divides food into groups and shows the recommended daily amounts needed for each food group. The food groups that should be eaten the most are the groups in the largest slices of the pyramid. The foods that should be eaten less often are in the narrow slices of the pyramid. MyPyramid also stresses the importance of physical activity in a healthy lifestyle. Let's explore each section to learn more about MyPyramid eating!

By using MyPyramid.gov, you can customize your diet for your age, your sex, and your physical activity level. Each person has individual dietary needs. To customize your diet, visit www.mypyramid.gov.

MyPyramid.gov
STEPS TO A HEALTHIER YOU

Breads, Cereals, Rice, and Pasta = The Grain Group

This group includes grains like bread, rice, oatmeal, grits, and noodles. These foods are naturally low in fat and provide us with the carbohydrates that our bodies need for energy. They also provide the vitamins, minerals, and fiber that we need to grow and stay healthy.

Did you know?
Our brains need carbohydrates to work at their best. Perhaps we should call grain foods "brain foods!"

Vegetables

Vegetables are great sources of vitamin A, vitamin C, folate (also called folic acid), and minerals such as iron and magnesium. Like grain foods, vegetables also contain little fat and lots of fiber. It is a good idea to include them in your meals and snacks. The more colorful the fruits and vegetables that you put on your plate, the better! Because vitamins A and C may keep us from developing chronic diseases, try to eat at least one yellow or orange vegetable (such as carrots or sweet potatoes) and one dark green vegetable (spinach, broccoli, romaine lettuce) every day. Other vegetables like corn, green beans, and potatoes are also good choices.

Did you know?
In addition to containing vitamins, minerals, and fiber, legumes are also a great source of protein.
Legumes can fit in both the vegetable or a meat groups of MyPyramid—
but not both at the same time.

Fruits

Packed with vitamins A and C and other nutrients like potassium and fiber, fruits are great-tasting, low-fat foods that are perfect choices for snacks and desserts! Try to eat two to four servings through the day. When possible, eat whole fruits instead of juice—you get more fiber! And unless you need extra calories, pick canned fruits that are packed in juice instead of syrup.

> ### *Did you know?*
> *You might be drinking sugary water? If you want juice, drink only juice that is labeled 100 percent fruit juice. Other juice drinks often contain a little bit of juice and a lot of added sugar.*

Meat, Poultry, Fish, Dry Beans, Eggs and Nuts = Protein for Growing Bodies!

Foods in this group supply our bodies with protein, B vitamins, iron, and zinc. Most meat and poultry choices should be lean or low in fat. Fish, nuts, and seeds contain healthy oils, so choose these foods often instead of meat or poultry.

> ### *Did you know?*
> *Meats, eggs, and nuts can fit in a low-fat, low-cholesterol eating plan. Just don't eat too much of them. Choose lean meats such as round steak or pork tenderloin. If eating poultry, select the light (white) meat and leave the skin off. For most people, eggs can be part of a low-fat diet as long as they eat a reasonable amount of them.*

Milk, Yogurt, and Cheese = Foods Your Bones Can Count On

Dairy products like milk, yogurt, and cheese contain protein, vitamins, and minerals. They contain a lot of calcium, which is essential for strong bones and healthy teeth. Choose fat-free or low-fat milk, yogurt, and cheese.

> ### *Did you know?*
> *People who watch their weight often substitute dairy products with diet sodas or other non-calorie drinks. Unfortunately, they may be doing more harm to their bones than good to their waistlines. For low-fat, high-calcium food choices, select skim milk, low-fat yogurt or reduced-fat cheeses. Watch out for ice cream; some brands contain a lot of saturated fat compared to the amount of calcium. Ice milk and frozen yogurt are usually better choices.*

Change Your Oils

Oils are not a food group but we do need some in small amounts. Get yours from fish, nuts, and vegetable oils such as corn, canola, and olive oil.

Use at Your Discretion

When you determine your food needs from mypyramid.gov, you will notice that you are given a set amount of "discretionary" calories. These are calories that can be used for foods that are not low in fat or added sugar. Everyone has a certain amount of these discretionary calories, but they will be based on your age, sex, and activity level. If you eat more discretionary calories than your body needs, you could gain weight—especially if you do not offset those extra calories with additional physical activity.

Fruits and Vegetables: Nutritious and Delicious

Fruits and vegetables are both tasty and nutritious. Fruits and most vegetables are fat-and sodium-free and can help us meet our daily need for several nutrients, including vitamin A, vitamin C, calcium, iron and fiber.

Vitamin A: This nutrient helps us see in the dark, promotes the growth and repair of tissues, prevents the drying of skin and eyes, and helps our body fight infections. The form of vitamin A found in plants, beta-carotene, acts as an antioxidant that may help prevent certain diseases.

Good Sources of Vitamin A (contains at least 10 percent Daily Value)*

Apricots	Guava
Avocado	Papaya
Black-eyed peas	Romaine lettuce
Brussels sprouts	Tangerine
Cherries	Tomato/tomato juice
Green peas	Watermelon

Excellent Sources of Vitamin A (contains at least 20 percent Daily Value)*

Broccoli	Nectarine
Cantaloupe	Persimmon
Carrots	Pumpkin
Chinese cabbage	Spinach
Collard greens	Sweet potato
Mango	Turnip greens
Mustard greens	Winter squash

Vitamin C: This nutrient, also called ascorbic acid, helps our bodies fight infections and heal wounds. Vitamin C helps our bodies absorb the mineral iron and may also protect our bodies from some diseases by acting as an antioxidant.

Good Sources of Vitamin C (contains at least 10 percent Daily Value)*

Asparagus	Nectarine
Avocado	Okra
Banana	Peach
Carrots	Pear
Green beans	Plum
Green peas	Pumpkin
Lentils	Spinach
Navy beans	Winter squash

Excellent Sources of Vitamin C (contains at least 20 percent Daily Value)*

Blueberries

Broccoli

Brussels sprouts

Cauliflower

Chinese cabbage

Collard greens

Grapefruit

Guava

Honeydew melon

Kiwi

Mango

Mustard greens

Orange

Orange juice

Papaya

Pineapple

Strawberries

Sweet peppers

Sweet potato

Swiss chard

Tangerine

Tomato

Turnip greens

Watermelon

Calcium: This mineral promotes development of strong bones and teeth. Calcium is needed so muscles (including the heart) will contract and calciums helps blood from a cut or wound clot. Nerve cells use calcium to carry impulses to neighboring cells.

<u>Good Sources of Calcium (contains at least 10 percent Daily Value)</u> *

Collard greens   Spinach   Turnip greens

Iron: Our bodies use iron to form hemoglobin and myoglobin, proteins that carry oxygen throughout our bodies.

<u>Good Sources of Iron (contains at least 10 percent Daily Value)</u> *

Black beans

Garbanzo beans (chickpeas)

Legumes (lima, navy, pinto, kidney and white beans)

Lentils

Spinach

Fiber: This nondigestible carbohydrate comes from plants in soluble or insoluble forms. Soluble fiber can lower blood cholesterol levels and may help the body regulate its blood sugar. Insoluble fiber, also called "roughage" helps prevent constipation by moving waste material through the digestive system.

Nutrition Facts for Healthful Eating

Want to learn more about the foods you eat? Look no further than the Nutrition Facts panel on a food package. This label can be a wealth of information for determining the amount of energy, fat and specific nutrients that are in a food. To better understand food labels, let's dissect a label into its different components.

Sample label for
Macaroni & Cheese

Nutrition Facts
Serving Size 1 cup (228g)
Serving Per Container 2

Amount Per Serving

Calories 250	Calories from Fat 110

% Daily Value*

Total Fat 12g	**18%**
Saturated Fat 3g	**15%**
Cholesterol 30mg	**10%**
Sodium 470mg	**20%**
Total Carbohydrate 31g	**10%**
Dietary Fiber 0g	**0%**
Sugars 5g	
Protein 5g	
Vitamin A	4%
Vitamin C	2%
Calcium	20%
Iron	4%

* Percent Daily Values are based on a 2,000 calorie diet. Your Daily Values may be higher or lower depending on your calorie needs:

	Calories:	2,000	2,500
Total Fat	Less than	65g	80g
Sat Fat	Less than	20g	25g
Cholesterol	Less than	300mg	300mg
Sodium	Less than	2,400mg	2,400mg
Total Carbohydrate		300g	375g
Dietary Fiber		25g	30g

Serving Size: This is the amount of a food that an average person might eat.

Servings Per Container: The number of servings that are in the package.

Calories: This is the amount of energy per serving.

Calories from Fat: This is the number of calories that come just from fat. To figure out the percent of calories from fat, simply divide the calories from fat by the total number of calories per serving.

Example: $\dfrac{\text{Calorie from Fat}}{\text{Calories}} = \dfrac{30}{90} = 33\%$

Thirty-three (33) percent of the calories in a serving of this food are from fat.

% Daily Value: The numbers down the right side of the Nutrition Facts panel are the percentage of the recommended amount of energy and nutrients that are provided per serving. On most labels, the % Daily Value is based on a 2,000 calorie diet. People with higher or lower energy needs may need different amounts of some nutrients.

Cholesterol: A fat-like substance found in animal products. Eating too much cholesterol can raise our risk of developing heart disease; try to consume no more than 300 milligrams per day.

Sodium: Often called "salt." For some people, eating large amounts of sodium may lead to high blood pressure. Canned and processed foods often have higher amounts of sodium than unprocessed foods. Try to limit the amount of sodium in your diet to 2,400 milligrams per day. This is equal to about 2 teaspoons of salt daily.

Total Carbohydrate: Carbohydrates are found in foods like bread, pasta, potatoes, fruits and vegetables.   Total carbohydrates include dietary fiber and sugars.

Dietary Fiber: Also called "roughage." Choosing foods high in fiber can help lower the risk for heart disease and cancer. Unfortunately, most people don't eat enough of this nutrient. To increase intake of fiber, consume whole grains, fruits and vegetables, and legumes.

Sugars: Includes natural sugars, such as those found in fruits, juices and milk products, and added sugars which are often found in candy and soda.

Protein: Our bodies need this nutrient for growth, repair of body tissues, and for general maintenance. Animal products like meat, milk and eggs and vegetable foods like grains and legumes give us plenty of protein to meet our needs. The lower part of the Nutrition Facts panel lets consumers know the amount of specific nutrients like vitamin A, vitamin C, calcium and iron that are found in a single serving of the food or beverage.

Vitamin A: Helps us see at night, is needed for bone and skin growth and development, and helps our bodies fight disease.

Vitamin C: Helps the body fight infections and heal wounds. May help prevent some diseases like cancer and heart disease.

Calcium: Promotes development of strong bones and teeth.

Iron: Helps carry oxygen throughout the body. Try to choose foods that have a low % Daily Value of fat, saturated fat, cholesterol and sodium. If some of your favorite foods have high amounts of fat, sodium or cholesterol, you can still eat them every once in a while.

Feast on Fiber For Better Health

What is fiber?

Fiber is a substance that is found in fruits, vegetables and grain products. The part of plant foods that we eat is called dietary fiber. There are two main types of dietary fiber, soluble and insoluble.

What is the difference between soluble and insoluble fiber?

Soluble fiber forms a gel when it is mixed with a liquid. When added to our daily diets, soluble fiber can help lower blood cholesterol levels. This may reduce the risk of getting heart disease. For people with diabetes, soluble fiber may help control blood sugar levels. Food sources of soluble fiber include oats, peas, beans, apples and oranges. Insoluble fiber often is called "roughage." This type of fiber gives bulk to stools, which makes it easier for the body to get rid of waste. Insoluble fiber also reduces the length of time that waste products are in the digestive system. This may reduce the risk for colon cancer. Sources of insoluble fiber include whole wheat foods, cauliflower, green beans, and the skins of fruits and root vegetables.

How much fiber do we need?

Adults should try to include 25 grams of fiber in their daily diets. Children and teens need amounts of dietary fiber that are equal to their ages plus five. For example, a six-year-old child would need 11 grams of fiber (6 + 5 = 11).

To increase the fiber in your diet:

- Eat a variety of plant-based foods including at least five servings of fruits and vegetables each day. This will provide both forms of fiber your body needs to stay healthy.

- Choose whole grain foods like 100 percent whole wheat bread, oatmeal and brown rice.

- Eat cooked dry beans and peas at least twice a week.

- Read food labels to compare the fiber content of food. Try to choose foods that have at least 10 percent of the daily value for fiber.

Important: When increasing the fiber in your diet, do it slowly and drink plenty of water!

Make wise food choices to make a big difference in the fiber content of your meals!

Before	After
Grilled cheese sandwich on white bread	Grilled cheese sandwich on 100 percent whole wheat bread
1 ounce of potato chips	3 cups of air-popped popcorn
1 regular-sized chocolate bar	1 medium-sized pear
8 ounces of water or tea	8 ounces of water or tea
4 grams of dietary fiber	12 grams of dietary fiber

To learn more about increasing your intake of dietary fiber, contact your local county Extension agent.

Apples: A Fast Food From Mother Nature

Apples, like other fruits, are nutritious and often inexpensive snack food options for people "on the go." When one compares the nutritional qualities of apples to other snacks, it's no wonder that some people think of apples as a healthy "grab-n-go" snack. Let's compare the nutritional value of a raw medium-sized apple to three chocolate chip cookies:

		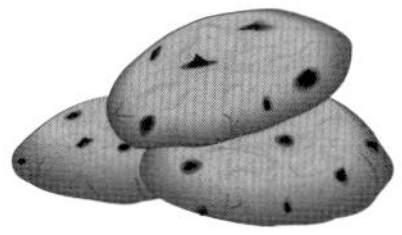
calories	81	154
grams of fat	0.5	7
% of calories from fat	5%	41%
milligrams of cholesterol	0	0
milligrams of sodium	0	96
grams of fiber	3.7	< 1
% daily value for vitamin C	13	0
% daily value for vitamin A	1	0

Apples fit in with other fruits on MyPyramid. Remember that grains, fruits, and vegetables should make up the majority of a person's diet.

Different Flavors and Uses of Apples

Apples differ in their flavor and texture; therefore, some varieties are better than others for snacks, salads, and desserts. The following chart describes some varieties of apples and how they can be used. For more information about apples, check with your local county Extension agent.

APPLE CHOICES - TAKE YOUR PICK!

Variety	Color/Texture	Taste	Use
Red Delicious	Bright to dark red, sometimes with stripes; has knobs at the base.	Sweet and juicy	Great for use in salads, garnishes, fruit trays and snacks.
Golden Delicious	Golden to light yellow green; skin is tender.	Rich apple flavor	Often called the "all purpose" cooking apple. Great for baking or eating raw!
Granny Smith	Bright to light green.	Tart and crisp	Great for snacking and for use in salads.
Gala	Yellow-orange under red striping to almost solid red.	Very sweet and aromatic; rich full flavor.	Great snack food! Small enough to keep in a purse, briefcase or backpack.
Braeburn	Color ranges from greenish-gold with red sections to almost solid red.	Very crisp and aromatic apple. Flavor is a blend of sweetness and tartness.	Great choice for salads and snacks.
Jonagold	A combination of Jonathan and Golden Delicious apples. Fruit has a yellow-green base and a blush stripe.	Tangy sweet flavor.	Great for eating fresh or for cooking.

Standardized Test Formatted Reading Passages

Plant Neighbors

One February, Mrs. Starr's class finished planting a new variety of corn in the school garden. Only one classmate, Jessica, had wanted to plant corn, beans and tomatoes. The rest of the class voted for only corn. Jessica kept thinking about what Farmer John had told the class when he visited earlier that year, "Plants are like people, they need neighbors too." He had told the group that just as people live and grow in neighborhoods with many different people, it is best for plants to grow in gardens with different types of plants.

Each week the class weeded and watered the garden. March came and went. The class worked hard. The month of April brought plenty of rain and in May the flowers bloomed. The corn plants showed thanks by growing big, beautiful ears of corn. Jessica stopped worrying almost.

Then it happened. The entire class could not believe it. Overnight, something had eaten on almost every single ear of corn. All that was left were bits and pieces of corn cob where the juicy, yellow kernels once grew. Jessica grabbed one of the ears and with her thumbs, carefully pulled away the green corn husks that covered the corn. "Nothing there," she said. Then she examined it more closely. She noticed a fat caterpillar curled up in a small hole where the yellow corn had been eaten away.

"I knew it, I knew it!" Jessica exclaimed,"Whatever are we going to do?" She looked around to the faces of classmates who could not believe their eyes. "My, my," were the only words Mrs. Starr could say. What was the class to do? "Let the caterpillars have the rest of the corn, too," another classmate said sadly.

After school Jessica walked over to Farmer John's place to tell him about the school garden and what had happened. Then she noticed many different kinds of beautiful, healthy, vegetable plants with brightly colored fruits. Jessica asked him for his secret of why his plants looked so healthy. "No secret," he said. "Just look around and tell me what you see." Each garden patch had at least three different kinds of plants: corn, squash and peas in one plot; carrots, tomatoes and onions in another; beans, strawberries and scented herbs in a third. Jessica was impressed.

Farmer John told her that plants with neighbors help one another. The neighbors shouldn't be the same kind of plant; they should be a variety of different plants. Some plants give off a scent that helps keep insects from feeding on them and other nearby plants. Plant neighbors also can help bring in beneficial insects to feed on the pesky insects. Farmer John also told her that the caterpillar that ate the class's corn only eats corn and wouldn't have eaten other planted vegetables. The corn's plant neighbors could have provided food to eat even if the corn was destroyed. "This is what our class needs to do. Give plants in our garden some neighbors," said Jessica.

The next day Jessica returned to school and shared what she had learned. Again, the class voted on what to plant in the school garden. This time, they gave the "thumbs up" to planting different kinds of vegetables in the garden: corn, beans and scented herbs, too.

Plant Neighbors

1. What was the story mostly about?

   ○ Tucker visiting Farmer John's place

   ○ Jessica finding tomatoes in the garden

   ○ A problem in the garden of Mrs. Starr's class

   ○ Farmer John's dog

2. Where did the story take place?

   ○ At the playground

   ○ At Jessica's house

   ○ In the school garden

   ○ In Tucker's garage

3. What does the word "beneficial" mean?

   ○ To make happy

   ○ Harmful

   ○ Helpful

   ○ To make sad

4. What did Jessica do after she visited with Farmer John?

   ○ Worked in the garden

   ○ Shared the information with the class

   ○ Looked in the ears of corn

   ○ Talked to her mom

5. What does the word "impressed" mean in this story?

   ○ Surprised

   ○ Disappointed

   ○ Angry

   ○ Worried

6. What did the class learn about gardening?

   ○ Plant only one kind of vegetable in the garden.

   ○ All insects are helpful.

   ○ It is important to plant many different kinds of vegetables in the garden.

   ○ Corn is not a plant.

Fruit and Vegetable Safety

You may have heard it is important to be "safe." There are many ways you can be safe. You can be safe by looking both ways before crossing the street. You can be safe by not talking to strangers. Have you been safe when you eat? Have you ever walked through the fruit and vegetable aisle in the grocery store, picked a grape and stuck it in your mouth?

There are many times, such as this, when brothers and sisters, even moms and dads, forget to eat foods safely. There's an easy way to remember to keep you and foods safe.

First, remember the letters J, M, G. The letter "J" stands for "Just clean the surface." The letter "M" is "Make sure to wash your hands." The letter "G" means "Garden veggies should be rinsed of soil, dirt and sand."

The second thing to do is practice what you've learned. *Just clean the surface.* Use warm water and soap every time you clean to clear away germs. Some germs are harmful bacteria or fungus that can cause us to get sick. Paper towels are good to use on countertops and cutting boards. This way, when you throw away the paper towel, the harmful germs are put in the trash where they belong, too.

Make sure to wash your hands. Wash your hands often, especially just before making or eating foods. Be sure to use warm running water and soap to wash away germs to keep you safe. Then dry your hands on a clean dish towel. Or, if you choose, use a fresh paper towel and throw it away. Never wipe your just washed hands on a dirty dish towel or paper towel. This puts germs back onto your hands that you just washed.

Garden veggies should be rinsed of soil, dirt and sand. Always wash the vegetables and fruit you pick from the garden because harmful germs may be on them. Don't just "pick them" and go. Remember to "wash them," too!

After you've done all these steps to protect you and your foods, then its safe to "eat them," too. Think of fresh fruits and vegetables from the garden as the **original fast foods** just "pick them, wash them, eat them and go!" So the next time you go to grab that grape at the store, first remember **J, M, G.**

Fruit and Vegetable Safety

1. In the story, who might have forgotten to eat foods safely?

   ○ Dog and cats

   ○ People

   ○ Dinosaurs

   ○ Mice

2. What can help you remember to keep foods safe?

   ○ Ride a bike.

   ○ Go to sleep.

   ○ Use the letters J, M, G.

   ○ Go to a party.

6. In the story, what is the reason it is a good idea to use paper towels?

   ○ It is important to recycle.

   ○ They can't be used again because they tear easily.

   ○ The germs on the paper towel are thrown away, too.

   ○ It is against the law to litter.

4. In the story, what is the first thing to remember to do just before eating?

   ○ Play with the dog.

   ○ Wash hands.

   ○ Put away the dishes.

   ○ Set the table.

5. Why is it important to wash fruits and vegetables?

   ○ They will last longer.

   ○ Germs are washed away.

   ○ They will grow larger.

   ○ It helps keep countertops clean.

6. What is meant by the key words "original fast foods"?

   ○ Fresh fruits and vegetables from the garden

   ○ A hamburger place

   ○ Cooked noodles

   ○ Cooked fruits and vegetables

The Veggie Fair

The end of the school year at Willow Oaks Elementary was exciting. Many of the students in Mrs. Taylor's fifth grade class and other classes were going to compete in the school's annual Veggie Fair. Every June the school held a competition to see who had grown the best tomatoes, peppers, squash and other vegetables.

Mrs. Taylor called her students "gardeners" because they all liked to grow vegetables and other plants in the class garden. The teacher assigned each gardener a partner and asked them to take care of a small section of the garden. The students could grow anything they wanted. Many chose to grow vegetables so they could compete in the Veggie Fair.

Tanisha and Sam were partners, and they decided to grow tomatoes in their section of the garden. Earlier in the spring, they had transplanted young tomato plants into the garden. They always checked the garden at least three times a week to pull any weeds that had grown and to water the plants if they were dry. They also fertilized their plants and looked for damage caused by insects. They even made a scarecrow to try to keep birds from eating the tomatoes.

On Monday, Sam and Tanisha saw posters in the hallways. They read all about the Veggie Fair and looked forward to having their special tomatoes in the contest.

**Willow Oaks Elementary School
Annual Veggie Fair**

Date: Friday, June 7
Time: 3:00 to 5:30 p.m.
Place: Cafeteria

Schedule:
3:00   Classes set out vegetables
3:30   Fair begins
4:00   Vegetables are weighed
4:30   Judging begins
5:00   Awards are announced

Rules:
1. All vegetables must be grown by students on campus.
2. Each entry must be labeled with student's name, class and grade level.
3. There will be awards for first, second and third place for each category.

Categories:
Awards will be given for the largest, heaviest, most colorful and tastiest of each type of vegetable entered.

Prizes:
Trophies and a pair of leather gardening gloves will be given to first place winners.

Second place winners will receive a red ribbon and leather gloves.

Third place winners will receive a white ribbon.

All others who enter the Veggie Fair will receive a yellow ribbon.

The Veggie Fair

1. What does the word "annual" mean in this story?

   ○ Night time

   ○ Once every year

   ○ Winter

   ○ Every month

2. Where does the Veggie Fair take place?

   ○ Cafeteria

   ○ Garden

   ○ Parking lot

   ○ Playground

3. What does the word "transplanted" mean in this story?

   ○ Pick tomatoes.

   ○ Put plants into the ground.

   ○ Pull weeds.

   ○ Water the plants.

4. What time does the judging begin?

   ○ 4:00

   ○ 4:30

   ○ 5:00

   ○ 5:30

5. Which of these is NOT a category in the fair?

   ○ Largest

   ○ Heaviest

   ○ Longest

   ○ Most colorful

6. What prize is awarded for third place?

   ○ Leather gloves

   ○ Red ribbon

   ○ White ribbon

   ○ Vegetable seeds

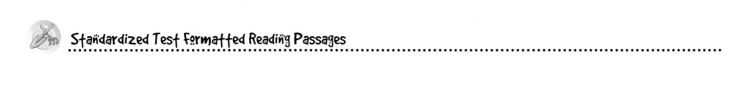
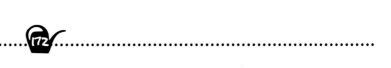

Registration Packet

JMG® REGISTRATION PACKET

The forms described below are used in registering youths and leaders in the Junior Master Gardener program, and for ordering completion certificates.

1. ***Junior Master Gardener Registration Agreement Form.*** The JMG Registration Agreement Form registers a properly organized and functional JMG group. The registration serves as a permit for use of the 4-H and JMG service marks, names, logos and emblems. It allows a group to function with all the rights and privileges of 4-H/JMG membership.

2. ***Junior Master Gardener Member Group Enrollment Form (JMG 1-5.061).*** The JMG program is expected to reach hundreds of youths across the nation and around the world. To document each youth's participation in the program, the teacher and/or leader must complete form JMG 1-5.061 for each group. JMG 1-5.061 will provide statistical data for state and federal governments for future funding and civil rights documentation.

Use these guidelines when completing the Junior Master Gardener Member Group Enrollment Form:
County Name: County in which the JMG program is being conducted
JMG Group Name: This name can be created by the youths (something catchy, or related to region)
JMG Group Teacher/Leader: Name of classroom teacher and/or leader (A registration form must be included for each person named.)

SECTION I: Unit Information
The JMG program can be organized in several ways:

Community:	A community 4-H club having club officers, regular monthly meetings, a community service project, project meetings, a club manager, parental participation and project leaders.
Project:	Same as a community club, except that it concentrates on only one project and expands into other projects after the original one.
School:	Same as community club, except that it is organized and conducted in school; members may be divided into several clubs of different ages.
Community Partnership:	Has the same structure as a community club and can be delivered in a school setting. However, the lead volunteers managing the club come from at least two other distinct organizations whose goal or project is to work with youths (e.g., Lions Club, Key Club, etc.).
Special Interest:	Organized or coordinated by Extension personnel and directed and/or taught by volunteer adult or youth leaders. The meetings are conducted in informal classroom settings with members participating in at least 20- to 60-minute learning sessions with the total learning time of at least 2 hours.
Curriculum Enrichment:	A learning activity in a classroom setting, led by school faculty, a staff member or a volunteer. The project consists of at least six learning experiences, each 20 to 60 minutes long. It uses the 4-H clover, and promotes other delivery methods in which youths can participate.
Camping:	Youth program in a structured, informal setting ranging from 1 full day to overnight.

ENP-Y: (Expanded Nutrition Program - Youth). Program designed to teach good nutrition and health. This program involves youth in all aspects of food production and consumption and can be delivered at schools as curriculum enrichment, in after-school programs or neighborhood groups, at recreation centers and summer day camps, and/or as displays at community health fairs.

Clover Kids (K-2): Informal educational program for youths ages 5 to 8 in kindergarten, first and second grades. This program is an introductory 4-H program for boys and girls.

SECTION II - Distribution of Member by:

Record information in this section as accurately as possible. Make sure that each person in the project is accounted for and that the totals in all four boxes match. If the RACE AND GENDER Section reflects that all participants are of the same race, then please complete the two questions under the box. This will provide civil rights documentation concerning the setting of the project and its accessibility to all races and sexes.

3. *Junior Master Gardener® Leader/Teacher Registration Form (JMG 2-1.056).* All teachers and volunteers must complete this form, which will be used to gather statistical information on all volunteers and teachers in the program. The back of the registration form is an optional volunteer screening process. After completing these forms, school teachers and officials are strongly encouraged to review the information about all volunteers before beginning the program.

The teachers and/or volunteer leaders should complete this form at the beginning of each new class of Junior Master Gardeners.

> You will receive from the JMG Program headquarters an official letter of registration for your group. A copy of your Registration Packet will be sent to your local Extension office for its records.

4. *JMG Completion Form.* All forms in the JMG Registration Packet should be mailed to the Junior Master Gardener headquarters.

Junior Master Gardener Program
2134 TAMU
College Station, Texas 77843-2134
(979) 845-8565
FAX (979) 845-8906
E-mail: programinfo@jmgkids.us

When members of your group complete the JMG curriculum requirements, order JMG Certificates by completing the JMG Completion Form and mailing it to the JMG Program headquarters at Texas A&M University. Certificates will be returned promptly so you can present them to the newest Junior Master Gardeners!

Please complete
and return the
following 4 pages.

Junior Master Gardener,
Registration Agreement Form

We request through this Registration Agreement Form to be an official JMG group. Our group has met all of the following criteria:

1. A minimum of five youths
2. One or more adult teacher/leader(s)
3. Suitable meeting facilities (classroom, garden area)
4. An official club or group name (JMG office reserves the right to modify name)

JMG group name desired _____

JMG site _____

County where JMG group is located _____

Designated JMG Teacher/Leader _____ Date _____

    Address _____ Telephone _____

    _____ e-mail _____

         City   State   ZIP

        (Notify of any address changes)

Submitting this form:

The group teacher/leader should complete this form and submit it to the JMG Program headquarters at Texas A&M University:

    International Junior Master Gardener Program
    2134 TAMU
    College Station, Texas 77843-2134
    Phone: (979) 845-8565
    Fax: (979) 845-8906

Educational programs conducted by the Texas AgriLife Extension Service serve people of all ages regardless of socioeconomic level, race, color, sex, religion, disability, or national origin.

Check:

❑ I have read the JMG Management Guide and agree to follow the JMG guidelines.

❑ I agree to assist in protecting the registered trademarks, service marks and copyright of the JMG program as described.

_____
        JMG Teacher/Leader signature   Date

Junior Master Gardener₅ Leader/Teacher Registration Form

JMG 2-1.065

JMG Group Name _____

Unit/Club Number _____

Check (✔) preference ☐ Mr. ☐ Mrs. ☐ Ms. ☐ Dr.

Name _____
    (Last)   (First)   (Middle Initial)

Mailing Address _____

City/Town _____ Zip Code _____

Phone Number: Home ( ) _____ Work ( ) _____

E-mail Address: _____
☐ Male   ☐ Female
☐ Adult ☐ Youth

This information is requested to gather statistics for compliance with nondiscrimination requirements.
Check (✔) only one

☐ 1. American Indian or Alaskan Native
☐ 2. Asian or Pacific Islander
☐ 3. Black - not Hispanic origin
☐ 4. Hispanic
☐ 5. White - not of Hispanic origin

Code   Project Name

10089   Junior Master Gardener

Years as a 4-H Leader (*including this year*) _____

Residence
Check (✔) only one

☐ 1. Rural/Farm
☐ 2. Town less than 10,000
☐ 3. City between 10,000 and 50,000
☐ 4. Suburb of city more than 50,000
☐ 5. Central city more than 50,000

Type of 4-H Unit
Check (✔) only one

☐ 1. Community
☐ 2. Project
☐ 3. School
☐ 4. Community Partnership
☐ 5. Clover Kids (K-2)
☐ 6. Special Interest
☐ 7. Curriculum Enrichment
☐ 8. Camping
☐ 9. ENP-Y

Major Leadership Responsibility

☐ 1. Club Manager
☐ 2. Project Leader
☐ 3. Activity Leader
☐ 4. JMG Volunteer (*specify*)
☐ 5. Other (*specify*) _____

4-H Alumni: ☐ Yes ☐ No

State _____
County _____

Do you work directly with youth?
☐ Yes ☐ No

_____   _____
Date   Signature

Educational programs of the Texas AgriLife Extension Service, The Texas A&M University System are open to people of all ages regardless of socioeconomic level, race, color, sex, religion, disability, or national origin.

The following information is REQUIRED in support of the Texas 4-H and Youth Development Program's commitment to continually guarantee the safety of the members during 4-H participation. I verify that I have been previously screened, including a criminal background check, and PASSED.

❏ Yes   ❏ No

If yes, by whom? _____ When (year)? _____

For what purpose? _____

If you did not pass, what restrictions were imposed? _____
_____

Volunteer Interest

Have you previously served as a 4-H volunteer?   ❏ Yes   ❏ No

If yes,   County _____ State _____ How many years? _____

Address at the time: _____

Personal Information *(To be completed by volunteers 18 years or older)*

Do you have a current/valid driver's license?   ❏ Yes   ❏ No

Do you have automobile liability insurance?   ❏ Yes   ❏ No

Other names you have used, including maiden name: _____

Have you ever been convicted of or received deferred adjudication for a violation of any local, state or federal law, other than (1) a minor traffic violation for which the fine was $200 or less, or (2) any offense which was finally settled in a Juvenile Court or under a Welfare Youth Offender Law? (This includes a plea of guilty or no contest.) ❏ Yes ❏ No If yes, *list all convictions below, from the oldest to the most recent.*			
Date of Conviction (MM/YR)	Misdemeanor (check if appropriate)	Felony (check if appropriate)	Offense (Do not use abbreviations)

References

1. Name_____ Address/City/ZIP _____ Phone_____

2. Name_____ Address/City/ZIP _____ Phone_____

3. Name_____ Address/City/ZIP _____ Phone_____

I hereby authorize veriFYI and/or its service provider and the Texas AgriLife Extension Service to request and receive any and all background information about or concerning me, including, but not limited to, my criminal history and my credit history, including a consumer report under the Fair Credit Reporting Act, 15 U.S.C 1681. I authorize the Texas AgriLife Extension Service or any of its components to make reference checks relating to my volunteer service. I understand that this information will be used to determine my eligibility as a volunteer/employee with the Texas AgriLife Extension Service.

The criminal history, as received from the reporting agencies, may include arrest and conviction data, as well as plea bargains and deferred adjudications and delinquent conduct committed as a juvenile. I understand that this information will be used, in part, to determine my eligibility for an employment/volunteer position with this organization. I also understand that as long as I remain an employee or volunteer here, the criminal history check may be repeated at any time. I understand that I will have an opportunity to review the criminal history as received by client/agency and that a procedure is available for clarification if I dispute the record as received. I also understand that the criminal history could contain information presumed to be expunged.

I further release and discharge veriFYI and its service provider and all of its subsidiaries, affiliates, officers, employees, contract personnel or associates from any and all claims and liability arising out of any request for information or records pursuant to this authorization and/or procurement of an investigative consumer report and understand that it may contain information about my character, general reputation, personal characteristics, and mode of living, whichever are applicable.

I understand that I have the right to make written request within a reasonable period of time to veriFYI for additional information concerning the nature and scope of the investigation. I acknowledge that I have voluntarily provided the above information for employment/volunteer purposes, and I have carefully read and understand this authorization.

My signature below indicates that:

• I give permission for photos or videotapes of myself to be reproduced for promotional or educational purposes.

• I give permission to participate in and/or complete surveys and evaluations that will be used to determine program effectiveness or to promote the program.

• I understand that participation in surveys and evaluations is voluntary and that I may choose not to participate in surveys or evaluations without any impact on my eligibility to serve with the Texas AgriLife Extension Service. I understand that I will be asked for my verbal assent before completing a survey or an evaluation.

_____   _____
Date   Volunteer Signature

JMG 1-5.061

Junior Master Gardener₋ Member Group Enrollment Form

Date _____ / _____ / _____

County Name _____

JMG Group Name _____

JMG Group Teacher/Leader _____

SECTION I - Unit Information: Type of 4-H organization (*Check only one*)

- ☐ 1. Community
- ☐ 2. Project
- ☐ 3. School
- ☐ 4. Community Partnership
- ☐ 5. Special Interest
- ☐ 6. Curriculum Enrichment
- ☐ 7. Camping
- ☐ 8. ENP-Y
- ☐ 9. Clover Kids (K-2)

SECTION II - Distribution of Members by: Totals in this section for age, residence and race and gender should all be the same.

RACE AND GENDER

	Males	Females	Totals
White - not of Hispanic origin			
Black - not of Hispanic origin			
American Indian or Alaskan Native			
Hispanic			
Asian or Pacific Islander			
Totals			

If all participants are of the same race, please answer the following questions:

Is this unit in a racially mixed community (at least two different racial groups)? ☐ Yes ☐ No

Is this unit integrated? ☐ Yes ☐ No

RESIDENCE

Residence	Number
Rural/Farm	
Town less than 10,000	
City between 10,000 and 50,000	
Suburb of city more than 50,000	
Central city more than 50,000	
Total	

JMG PROJECT CODE

Code	10089
Males	
Females	

AGE

Age	Number
Under 9	
9	
10	
11	
12	
13	
14	
15	
16	
17	
18	
19	

JMG® Junior Master Gardener® Completion Form

(For Certificates - Duplicate as Needed)

Upon completion of the JMG curriculum requirements, fill out this form to request JMG Certificates for your group members. Mail the completed form to Junior Master Gardener Program, 2134 TAMU, 225 HFSB, Texas A&M University, College Station, Texas 77843-2134.

Circle certification earned by these students:

—— JMG Level One ——

certifications available from the JMG Teacher/Leader Guide:

A. Certified Junior Master Gardener
(for students completing requirements in all eight chapters)

Golden Ray Series Certification in:
(for students completing requirements in a smaller unit of study)

B. Plant Growth & Development

C. Soils & Water

D. Insects & Plant Diseases

E. Ecology & Environmental Horticulture

F. Landscape Horticulture

G. Fruit & Nutrition

H. Vegetables & Herbs

I. Life Skills & Career Exporation

J. *new!* Growing a Vegetable Garden
other Golden Ray Series recognition certificate options:

K. Health & Nutrition from the Garden

L. Wildlife Gardener

M. Literature from the Garden

—— JMG Level Two ——

certifications available from Operation Thistle or Operation WATER

N. Plant Growth & Development

O. Soils & Water

Name											

Estimate the total number of hours of service your group performed.*

_____ total hours of service

This is just a rough estimate of the number of hours your group worked to complete your service project(s) multiplied by the number of youths taking part in the effort. For example, if your class spent about six total hours working on a project and there are 20 students in your group, that would be a total of 120 hours of service contributed by your group.

Teacher/leader name: _____

Signature: _____ Date: _____

Certificates should be mailed to the following address:

_____ City _____ State _____ ZIP _____

Phone (___) _____

email: _____

Registration Packet

Visit **www.jmgkids.us** to learn about certification options and requirements. Allow 2–3 weeks for return of needed certificates.

Looking for More Fun for Your JMG Kids?????

VISIT THE JMG WEB PAGE!

www.jmgkids.us

or call Toll free (888) 900-2577
Order JMG items at http://agrilifebookstore.org

JMG YOUTH HANDBOOKS	**JMG APPAREL**
GOLDEN RAY SERIES CURRICULUM	**JMG RECOGNITION ITEMS**
JMG TEACHER/LEADER GUIDES	**NOVELTY ITEMS**

Puchases can be made with check, credit cards, or purchase order.
Information on prices, shipping/handling, and delivery are available from the website.

*JMG...Cultivating youth and communities through gardening*sm

Acknowledgments

JMG Golden Ray Series *"Health and Nutrition from the Garden"*

Project Team

Shelley Siegenthaler Genzer
> JMG Project Coordinator, "Health and Nutrition from the Garden,"
> Extension Assistant-Horticulture, The Texas A&M University System

Lisa A. Whittlesey
> JMG Junior Master Gardener Coordinator, Extension Program Specialist-Horticultural Sciences,
> The Texas A&M University System

Cheryl Supak
> Extension Associate, Texas AgriLife Extension Service, The Texas A&M University System

Authors

Shelley Siegenthaler Genzer

Randy Seagraves, JMG Curriculum Coordinator, Extension Program Specialist-Horticultural Sciences,
> The Texas A&M University System

Jenna Anding, Assistant Professor and Extension Nutrition Specialist,
> The Texas A&M University System

Lisa Whittlesey

Olivia Aguilar, Graduate Student, Department of Horticultural Sciences, Texas A&M University

Glen Graves, Harris County Master Gardener, The Texas A&M University System

Cynthia Klemmer, Garden Program Facilitator, Department of Horticultural Sciences,
> Texas A&M University

Shari Koch, Graduate Assistant, Department of Horticultural Sciences, Texas A&M University

Sarah Lineberger, Graduate Assistant, Department of Horticultural Sciences, Texas A&M University

Debra Reed, Assistant Professor and Extension Nutrition Specialist, The Texas A&M University System

Sharon Robinson, Assistant Professor and Extension Nutrition Specialist,
> The Texas A&M University System

Connie Sebesta, Vegetable and Fruit Improvement Center, Administrative Assistant,
> Department of Horticultural Sciences, Texas A&M University

Peggy Van Laanen, Professor and Extension Program Leader for Food and Nutrition,
> The Texas A&M University System

Al Wagner, Associate Department Head and Extension Program Leader for Horticultural Sciences,
> The Texas A&M University System

Carolyn Walton-Robinson, Graduate Assistant, Department of Horticultural Sciences,
> Texas A&M University

Douglas F. Welsh, Professor and Extension Horticulturist, Department of Horticultural Sciences

Dotty Woodson, County Extension Agent-Horticulture, Tarrant County,
> The Texas A&M University System

Jayne Zajicek, Professor and Associate Department Head, Horticultural Sciences,
> Texas A&M University

REVIEWERS

Jenna Anding, Extension Program Leader for Nutrition and Food Science

David Byrne, Professor, Department of Horticultural Sciences, Texas A&M University

Luis Cisneros-Zevallos, Assistant Professor, Department of Horticultural Sciences, Texas A&M University

Sam Cotner, Head, Department of Horticultural Sciences, Texas A&M University

Frank Dainello, Professor and Extension Horticulturist, The Texas A&M University System

Alice Kirk, Extension Program Specialist–Child Health and Wellness

Cynthia Klemmer

R. Daniel Lineberger, Professor, Department of Horticultural Sciences, Texas A&M University

Sarah Lineberger, former Graduate Assistant, Department of Horticultural Sciences, Texas A&M University

Evelyn Neier, Associate Specialist, Family Nutrition Program/Junior Master Gardener/4-H Youth Development, Kansas State Research & Extension

Debra Reed, former Associate Professor and Extension Nutrition Specialist

Sharon Robinson, Associate Professor and Extension Nutrition Specialist

Connie Sebesta, Administrative Assistant, Vegetable and Fruit Improvement Center

Cheryl Supak, former Better Living for Texans Program Director

Peggy Van Laanen, former Professor and Extension Program Leader for Food and Nutrition

Al Wagner, Professor and Extension Food Technology Specialist

Douglas F. Welsh, Extension Program Leader for Horticulture

Lynn White, former Professor and Extension Consumer/Family Science Specialist

Jayne Zajicek, Growing Minds Program

SPECIAL THANKS TO

Jillian Gray, Program Assistant, Tarrant County, for her enthusiasm and in providing valuable activity feedback

Dotty Woodson, County Extension Agent-Horticulture, Tarrant County, for her horticultural expertise and leadership

Joe Medrano, Program Assistant, Cameron County

Tom Baranowski, Children's Nutrition Research Center, Houston, Texas

Jayne M. Zajicek, Growing Minds Program, for allowing her graduate student to evaluate the curriculum

Sarah Lineberger, for the initial nutritional attitude study and laying the groundwork used in development of this project

Shari Koch, for agreeing to study the nutritional attitudes of youths involved in the evaluation

Carolyn Walton-Robinson, for maintenance and codevelopment of the JMG Junior Master Gardener Web site

All of the youth participants who took part in helping to evaluate this curriculum

CURRICULUM STUDY SITES

Tarrant County Extension
Cameron County Extension

NUTRITIONAL ATTITUDE EVALUATION SITES

Tarrant County Extension
Cameron County Extension
Angelina County Extension
Hildago County Extension
Martin County Extension
Young County Extension

CONTRIBUTING PHOTOGRAPHS

Sam Cotner

Frank Dainello

Al Wagner

Joseph Novak, Senior Lecturer, Department of Horticultural Sciences, Texas A&M University

John Jackman, Professor and Extension Entomologist, The Texas A&M University System

Bastiaan Drees, Professor and Extension Entomologist, The Texas A&M University System
     Texas A&M University Entomology Department
Entomology Web site http://EntoCentennial.tamu.edu
University Photographic Services

PHOTOGRAPHY MODELS

Kory Davis, Yvette Esquivel, and Taylor Whittlesey

LEAD ILLUSTRATION

Jackson Price, Communications Specialist, Texas Transportation Institute, The Texas A&M University System

EDITING

Gale Norman, Agricultural Communications

PRODUCTION MANAGER

John Colvin, Prepress Manager, Newman Printing Company, Inc.

PAGE DESIGNERS

Connie Gosch, Digital/Layout Artist, Newman Printing Company, Inc.

Jerry Knucker, Graphic Designer, Agricultural Communications

Stephanie Schwerdtfeger, Digital/Layout Artist, Newman Printing Company, Inc.

COVER DESIGN

Lori Ciano-Colvin, Graphic Designer, Words & Pictures

Fruit and Veggie Mania Card Game

Game Rules

Separate the cards using scissors, cut along the dotted lines.

Each player receives seven cards to start the game. The remaining cards are placed face-down in the "Pantry Pile" on the game board. The object of the game is to eat the cards by playing them out of players' hands.

A card may be played only if it has something in common with the card that was played before it. There are five ways a card can be in common with the previously played card; if both cards:

✿ have the same fruit or vegetable on the faces of the cards, OR

✿ have at least one nutrient amount that matches, OR

✿ are the same plant part (leaf, stem, root, flower, fruit), OR

✿ have the same growing season (cool season or warm season), OR

✿ have one edible color in common.

If a player cannot play a card that matches the card showing, then that player must draw a card from the "Pantry Pile." If the drawn card is a match, the card is played; otherwise, the player loses his/her turn.

There are special cards that can be played. They are:

Pyramid Power card – can only be played when no cards in a player's hand have anything in common with the card just played. The gardener that plays this card chooses the fruit or vegetable to resume play.

Pyramid Pop card – can be played at anytime. Allows a player to play two cards at one time. The player plays a card along with the Pyramid Pop card. The next player has to pick up the Pyramid Pop card and loses his/her turn. Playing resumes with the fruit or vegetable card that is showing (the fruit or vegetable card played by the Pyramid Pop card player). *The food item on the Pyramid Pop card represents sweets, fatty foods, and oils and fats. These foods should be eaten only in small amounts.*

Tasty Turn Around card – can be played at anytime. This card allows a player to switch the direction of play. For example, if playing in a clockwise direction, then players would start playing in a counter-clockwise direction.

Second Serving card – can be played at anytime. When this card is played, the next player must draw two cards from the "Pantry Pile" and loses his/her turn.

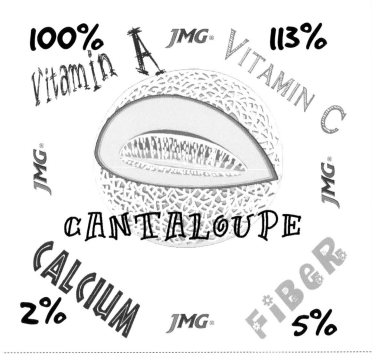

100% Vitamin A   *JMG*   113% VITAMIN C

CANTALOUPE

CALCIUM 2%   *JMG*   FiBeR 5%

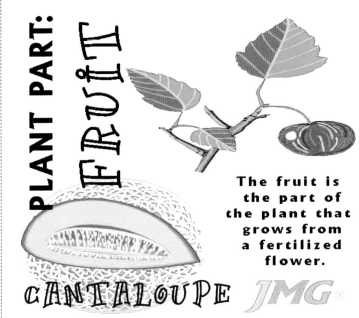

PLANT PART: FRUIT

The fruit is the part of the plant that grows from a fertilized flower.

CANTALOUPE   *JMG*

WaRM SeaSoN

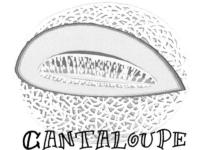

JMG   CANTALOUPE

edible colors: CANTALOUPE

ORANGE

JMG

PYRAMID   *JMG*

MyPyramid.gov
STEPS TO A HEALTHIER YOU

POWER

JMG

Sweets, fatty foods, and oils should be eaten only in very small amounts.

French Fries

PYRAMID POP

If you are given this card, it must be played as your next turn.

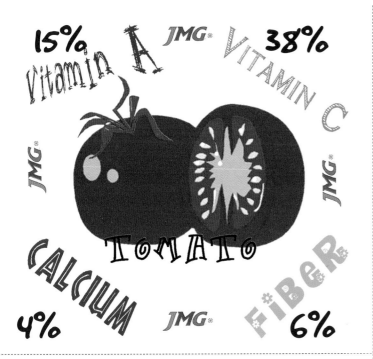

15% **Vitamin A** *JMG®* 38% **VITAMIN C**

JMG® *JMG®* *JMG®*

TOMATO

CALCIUM **FIBER**

4% *JMG®* 6%

PLANT PART: FRUIT

The fruit is the part of the plant that grows from a fertilized flower.

TOMATO *JMG®*

WARM SEASON

JMG® **TOMATO**

edible colors:

TOMATO

YELLOW
RED
ORANGE *JMG®*

PYRAMID

JMG®

MyPyramid.gov
STEPS TO A HEALTHIER YOU

POWER

JMG®

French Fries

Sweets, fatty foods, and oils should be eaten only in very small amounts.

PYRAMID POP

If you are given this card, it must be played as your next turn.

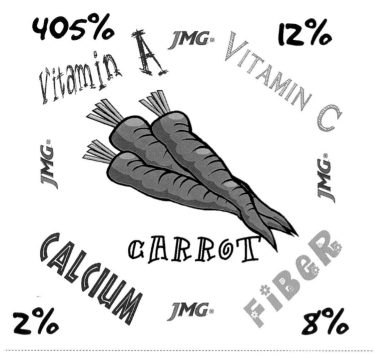

405%

Vitamin A

JMG®

12%

VITAMIN C

JMG®

JMG®

CARROT

CALCIUM

2%

JMG®

FiBeR

8%

JMG®

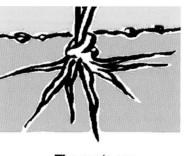

PLANT PART: ROOTS

The roots are the part of the plant that draw moisture and nutrients from the soil and anchor the plant to the ground.

CARROT

JMG®

COOL SEASON

JMG®

CARROT

edible colors:

CARROT

ORANGE

MAROON

YELLOW

JMG®

PYRAMID

JMG®

MyPyramid.gov
STEPS TO A HEALTHIER YOU

POWER

JMG®

Sweets, fatty foods, and oils should be eaten only in very small amounts.

french fries

PYRAMID POP

If you are given this card, it must be played as your next turn.

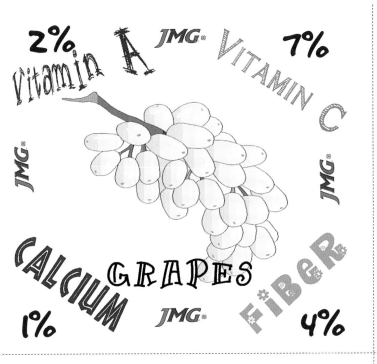

2% Vitamin A 7% VITAMIN C

CALCIUM GRAPES FiBeR

1% 4%

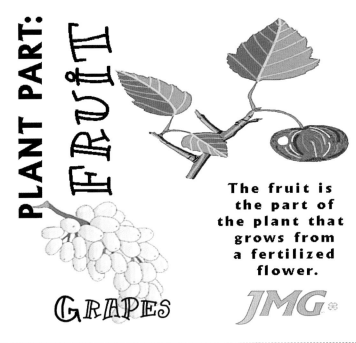

FRUIT

The fruit is the part of the plant that grows from a fertilized flower.

GRAPES

JMG

WaRM SeaSoN

JMG GRAPES

edible colors:

GRAPES

PURPLE

RED

GREEN

JMG

PYRAMID

MyPyramid.gov
STEPS TO A HEALTHIER YOU

POWER

Sweets, fatty foods, and oils should be eaten only in very small amounts.

PYRAMID POP

If you are given this card, it must be played as your next turn.

8% Vitamin A

JMG®

560% Vitamin C

JMG®

JMG®

BELL PEPPER

CALCIUM

2%

JMG®

FiBeR

7%

PLANT PART: Fruit

The fruit is the part of the plant that grows from a fertilized flower.

BELL PEPPER

JMG®

WaRM SeaSoN

JMG®

BELL PEPPER

edible colors:

BELL PEPPER

ORANGE

RED

PURPLE

GREEN

YELLOW

JMG®

PYRAMID

JMG®

MyPyramid.gov
STEPS TO A HEALTHIER YOU

POWER

JMG®

French Fries

Sweets, fatty foods, and oils should be eaten only in very small amounts.

PYRAMID POP

If you are given this card, it must be played as your next turn.

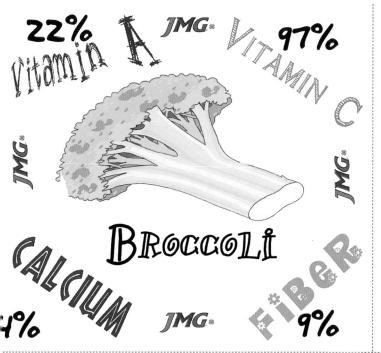

22% **Vitamin A** JMG® 97% **Vitamin C**

JMG®

JMG®

JMG®

Broccoli

Calcium

4%

JMG®

Fiber

9%

Flower

The flower is the part of the plant that is pollinated so that new plants can be produced.

Broccoli

JMG®

COOL SEASON

JMG®

Broccoli

edible colors:

Broccoli

GREEN

JMG®

JMG®

Tasty TurnAround

This card reverses the direction of the order each player takes a turn.

Second Serving

Play this card and the next person's turn must be used drawing two new cards.

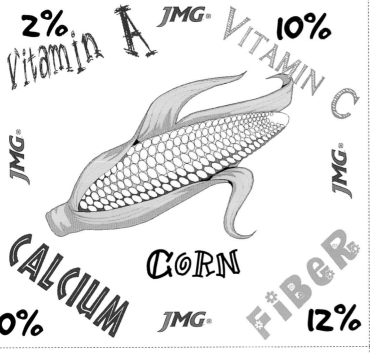

2% **Vitamin A** *JMG®* 10% **VITAMIN C**

JMG® *JMG®*

CALCIUM **FiBeR**

0% *JMG®* 12%

CORN

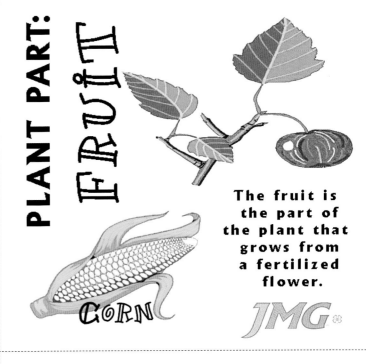

PLANT PART: **FRUIT**

The fruit is the part of the plant that grows from a fertilized flower.

CORN *JMG®*

WaRM SeaSoN

JMG® **CORN**

edible colors: **CORN**

YELLOW

RED

WHITE *JMG®*

JMG®

Tasty TurnAround

This card reverses the direction of the order each player takes a turn.

Second Serving

Play this card and the next person's turn must be used drawing two new cards.

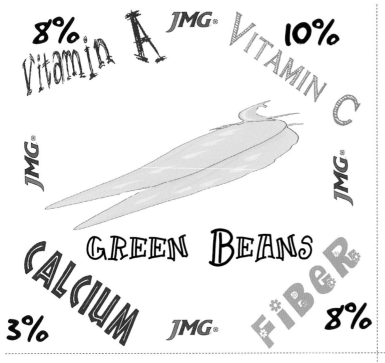

8%. **Vitamin A** *JMG*® **Vitamin C** 10%

JMG®

GREEN BEANS

CALCIUM *JMG*® **FIBER**

3% 8%

PLANT PART: FRUIT

The fruit is the part of the plant that grows from a fertilized flower.

GREEN BEANS *JMG*®

WARM SEASON

JMG® GREEN BEANS

edible colors: GREEN BEANS

GREEN

JMG®

JMG®

Tasty TurnAround

This card reverses the direction of the order each player takes a turn.

Second Serving

Play this card and the next person's turn must be used drawing two new cards.

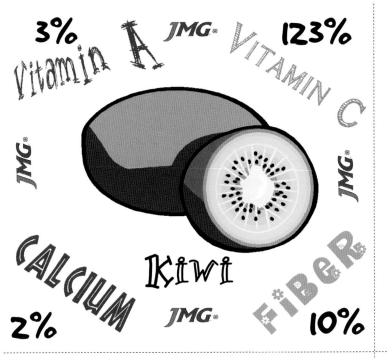

3% Vitamin A JMG® 123% VITAMIN C

JMG®

CALCIUM

2%

Kiwi

JMG®

FiBeR

10%

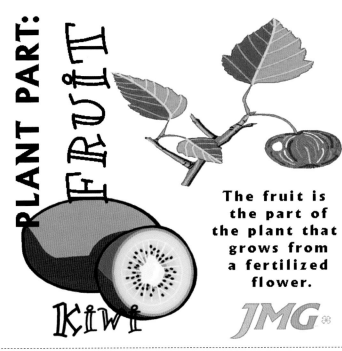

PLANT PART: FruiT

The fruit is the part of the plant that grows from a fertilized flower.

Kiwi

JMG®

WaRM SeaSoN

JMG®

Kiwi

edible colors:

Kiwi

GREEN

JMG®

JMG®

Tasty TurnAround

This card reverses the direction of the order each player takes a turn.

Second Serving

Play this card and the next person's turn must be used drawing two new cards.

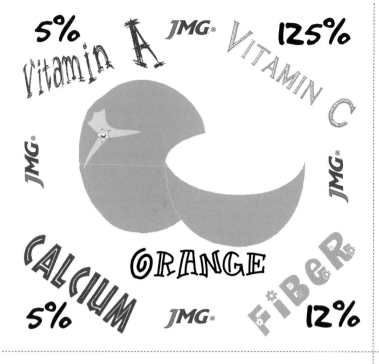

5% **Vitamin A** *JMG®* 125% *VITAMIN C*

JMG®

JMG®

CALCIUM
5% *JMG®*

ORANGE

FiBeR
12%

PLANT PART: FRUIT

The fruit is the part of the plant that grows from a fertilized flower.

ORANGE *JMG®*

WaRM SeaSoN

JMG®

ORANGE

edible colors: ORANGE

ORANGE

JMG®

Tasty TurnAround

This card reverses the direction of the order each player takes a turn.

Second Serving

Play this card and the next person's turn must be used drawing two new cards.

Vitamin A 1%   JMG   VITAMIN C 40%

JMG

JMG

CALCIUM 1%   PINEAPPLE   JMG   FiBeR 8%

PLANT PART: FRUIT

The fruit is the part of the plant that grows from a fertilized flower.

PINEAPPLE   JMG

WaRM SeaSoN

JMG   PINEAPPLE

edible colors:

PINEAPPLE

YELLOW

JMG

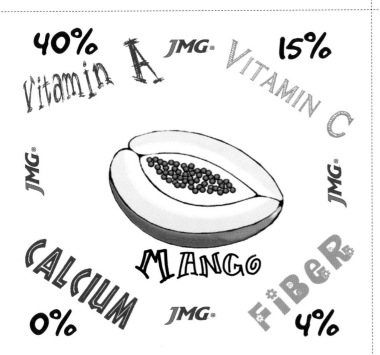

Vitamin A 40%   JMG   VITAMIN C 15%

JMG

JMG

CALCIUM 0%   MANGO   JMG   FiBeR 4%

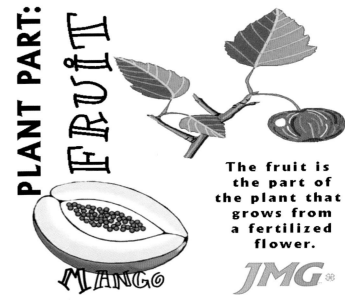

PLANT PART: FRUIT

The fruit is the part of the plant that grows from a fertilized flower.

MANGO   JMG

147% **Vitamin A** *JMG* 15% **VITAMIN C**

JMG

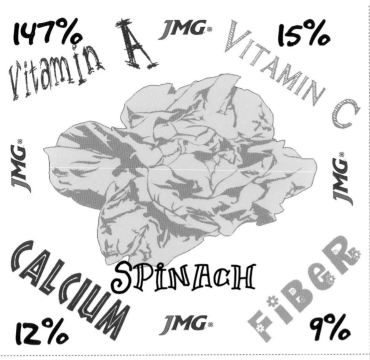

SPINACH

CALCIUM *JMG* FIBER

12% 9%

The leaves are the parts of the plant that absorb light for photosynthesis.

SPINACH *JMG*

COOL SEASON

JMG SPINACH

---

edible colors:

SPINACH

GREEN

JMG

WARM SEASON

JMG MANGO

---

edible colors:

MANGO

YELLOW

JMG

560% **Vitamin A** JMG. 47% *VITAMIN C*

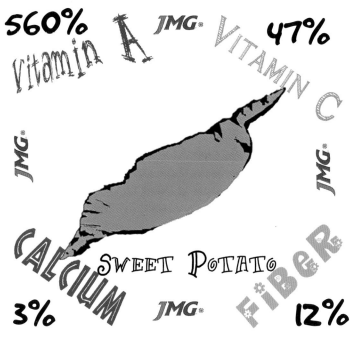

JMG.

JMG.

CALCIUM   Sweet Potato   FiBeR

3%   JMG.   12%

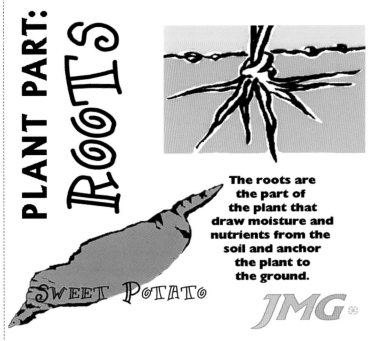

The roots are the part of the plant that draw moisture and nutrients from the soil and anchor the plant to the ground.

Sweet Potato

JMG.

WaRM SeaSoN

JMG.

Sweet Potato

edible colors:

Sweet Potato

ORANGE

JMG.